FERTILITY
· PASTURES ·

FERTILITY
· PASTURES ·

Herbal leys as the basis
of soil fertility and animal health

Newman Turner

With a new foreword by Joel Salatin

Acres U.S.A.
Austin, TX

Fertility Pastures

Acres U.S.A.
P.O. Box 91299
Austin, Texas 78709 U.S.A.
(512) 892-4400 • fax (512) 892-4448
info@acresusa.com • www.acresusa.com

Printed in the United States of America

Publisher's Cataloging-in-Publication

Turner, Newman, 1913-1964
Fertility pastures / Newman Turner. Austin, TX, ACRES U.S.A., 2009
    Reprint. Originally published: London: Faber and Faber Limited, 1951.
    xxvi, 198 pp., 23 cm.
    Includes Index
    Includes Bibliography
    Incudes Illustrations
    ISBN 978-1-60173-011-4 (trade)

1. Organic farming. 2. Alternative agriculture. 3. Sustainable agriculture. 4. Agricultural ecology. 5. Organic fertilizers. I. Turner, Newman, 1913-1964 II. Title.

SB199.T8 2009   633.2

A Note from the Publisher . . .

It is with particular pride that we make the classic writings of Newman Turner on grass farming and natural health for cattle available to a new generation of organic farmers and graziers. A particularly sad note in our modern era of instantaneous digital information retrieval is the tendency to ignore older works. University librarians shake their heads in dismay as they note that students and researchers tend to delve into digital archives — many dating no further back than the 1990s — and scoff at any suggestion of entering the library stacks and dusting off vintage books.

Priceless insight can be found in the herd research of Randleigh Farm, the soils research of Professor William Albrecht, the traditional farming systems observations of F.H. King, or the pioneering writings of Sir Albert Howard, Lady Eve Balfour, André Voisin, Friend Sykes, Louis Bromfield, J.I. Rodale and others. Students of these great farmer-scientists, and others, quickly discern a level of sophistication still unparalleled by our modern-era reductionist scientists.

Most of the writings of these organic method pioneers were born during the beginning of the chemical era of agriculture. There was a fork in the road then, either toward sophisticated, diversified natural farming systems or chemical-based factory-style agriculture. History has recorded the fallout of the poor choice made back then in the statistics of depleted soils, poor crop quality, epidemic cancer and degenerative disease, and crippled farm economies.

Increasingly farmers and consumers are returning to healthier forms of food and farming. And the visionaries who stood firm at that earlier fork in the road still stand waiting to point the way to a new future.

In republishing Turner's writings, we've fought the temptation to modernize, Americanize, or heavily update these classic works. Obviously, currencies and their values change over a half-century. There are a few inputs and technologies that subsequent study have deemed inappropriate. And North American readers will have to pick up a few words of vocabulary as they translate from British English to American English. We present these books as they were published in the 1950s with only the slightest of annotation. A discerning reader who takes these books for what they are will walk away with a new understanding of the power and sophistication of the organic method and the beauty of farming in harmony with nature. And that reader will find lasting inspiration in Turner's love of land and beast and his plucky attitude toward the conventional wisdom of his day.

A special word of thanks must go to the sons of Newman Turner — Adam Newman Turner, Giles Newman Turner and Roger Newman Turner — for their trust in our stewardship of their father's written legacy and assistance in bringing these works back into reach of readers everywhere. The late American organic pioneer Bargyla Rateaver published editions of some of these works in the 1970s, which, like the originals, are now out of print. Like Newman Turner, she was clearly ahead of her time.

E.M. Forster wrote, "I suggest that the only books that influence us are those for which we are ready, and which have gone a little further down our particular path than we have yet got ourselves." Perhaps it is fitting that Newman Turner's farming and pasturing methods and insights into herd health are unveiled again today — after hiding in plain sight for these past decades — as interest in his brand of farming is at groundswell level. Untold numbers of new grass farmers will benefit from standing on this great's shoulders and learning anew from this simple farmer-scientist who has "gone a little further down our particular path than we have yet got ourselves."

Read, enjoy, and learn from the experiences and wisdom of fellow grass farmer Newman Turner.

October 2008   FRED C. WALTERS
AUSTIN, TEXAS

Foreword

Anyone who starts down an unconventional path has an insatiable thirst for a support group of mentors. The road less traveled can be lonely. Finding guides is critical because the unbeaten path can be hard to find and hard to follow.

When I began following my grandfather and then my father into this strange and wonderful grass farming world, I needed encouragement just like every young person. And especially young people who chart an unpopular course.

For the most part, my mentors were no longer alive in the late 1970s when, as a young man, I stood on my ancestors' shoulders and headed in their direction. Yes, my father's encouragement helped, but I yearned for more confirmation.

I found it in the writings of Louis Bromfield, J.I. Rodale, and Sir Albert Howard. But the one that fired my soul was this little classic by Newman Turner. He was a farmer's farmer and had a spirit similar to my own.

Bromfield was too wealthy to be my soul mate. Rodale too academic. Howard too Extension oriented. Turner was a true blue farmer.

And as you will discover in these pages that live as surely today as the day he tapped them out on a typewriter (yes, back then), he is not afraid to question icons of modern agriculture. Things like soil samples. He dared to question production-oriented goals, favoring instead balanced goals — economics and ecology.

A true innovator, Turner was a master observer. He had no agenda except to heal the soil, heal the land, and heal his country. He held heritage wisdom in awe, not ready to jump on a machine just because it promised efficiency. He saw haymaking, for example, as an art form and was far more interested in making good hay than in making mountains of hay.

He understood the heritage relationship between cows and grass. But not just grass — herbs and legumes as well. He is the kind of farmer that thrills my soul. His words energize though they be from another culture and another time. He calls his farming *ley farming,* a term denoting variety and rotation. I call mine a pasture salad bar.

That's just wordsmithing for a different culture and a different time. I'd like to think that if he heard about my salad bar pasture, he would smile mischievously and with a twinkle in his eye, say: "Now that's a clever way to describe it." These mentors of my past, these heroes who live through sheer strength of righteous farming articulated passionately in books like *Fertility Pastures,* seem to hover around my daily thoughts like angels, applauding, encouraging, challenging and leading still.

This little volume is still one of my favorites, and I recommend it to any student seeking all that is good and noble about pasture-based livestock farming. Newman Turner, teach us again.

February 2008   JOEL SALATIN
                                                            SWOOPE, VIRGINIA

Joel Salatin is a farmer and author
of several books on pasture-based farming.

Reading Newman Turner . . .

Modern-day readers might have to adjust their vocabulary as they read this historic work, particularly those readers in North America. Following are a few thoughts on some specific terms Turner uses:

Catarrh – read as *inflammation of a mucous membrane.*

Corn – read as *grains.*

Dredge corn – read as *mixed cereals and legumes.*

Herbal ley – Today this would be called a rotational grazing cell, a paddock, or pasture. He emphasized a mix of grasses, clover and herbs. Turner made use of standard grasses such as timothy, meadow fescue, orchard grass and perennial ryegrass. Into this he added the herbs chicory, yarrow, plantain, burnet and sheep's parsley as they are deep rooted and concentrate a wide range of minerals, more so than the grasses.

Ley – read as *temporary pasture,* or a rotational cell or paddock.

Lucerne – read as *alfalfa.*

Maize – read as *corn.*

Manuring – read as *fertilizing.* What would be called *manure spreading* in North America would be described by Turner as *manuring with FYM (farmyard manure).*

Project – read as *program.*

Pulses – read as *legumes.*

About the Author

Frank Newman Turner was one of the founders of the modern environmental movement and published some of the first organic farming and gardening magazines. He founded *The Farmer,* the first organic quarterly magazine "published and edited from the farm," became a founding council member of the Soil Association, the U.K.'s leading regulator of organic standards, and served as president of an early organic horticultural organization. As a farmer, he received numerous awards in animal breeding and horticulture. A true visionary, many of his agricultural innovations are only now being rediscovered by the new wave of organic farmers and graziers.

He was born in September 1913, the eldest son of tenant farmers near Barnsley, Yorkshire, England. After graduating in agriculture and dairying at Leeds University, he became an inspector with the Potato Marketing Board. His journalistic skills soon became apparent, and he wrote regular columns for the British publications *Farmers Weekly* and *Farmer and Stockbreeder.* He met his future wife Lorna while he was on a business trip to Cornwall, and they married in 1939.

AN INDEPENDENT MIND

The dedication in F. Newman Turner's first book, *Fertility Farming,* is, "To my mother, who taught me to think for myself." This quality came to the fore as World War II approached, and he registered as a conscientious objector. He had become a Quaker and attended lectures by Dick Sheppard and other prominent pacifists of the time. Humanitarian principles were to guide him for the rest of his life. In 1940, he and Lorna, with their newborn son, moved to the edge of the Chilton Polden Hills in Somerset, England, where he was to manage Goosegreen, a mixed farm of about 200 acres, for conscientious objectors. Here he began experiments in organic husbandry inspired by the writings and personal encouragement of Sir Albert Howard, the author of the classics *An Agricultural Testament* and *Farming and Gardening for Health or Disease.*

When the war ended Turner bought Goosegreen and continued his experiments in creating "health from the soil up." The plow soon became redundant. He believed that fertility lay in the subsoil and was best sustained by minimal disturbance. Deep-rooting herbal leys, or planting blends for pasture, formed the basis of healthy stock — in Turner's case a herd of prize-winning pedigree Jerseys. Ailments among the cattle and draft horses — and children — were treated by fasting, enemas and dosing with herbal infusions.

F. Newman Turner launched the magazine *The Farmer* in 1946. It soon gained a devoted, if small, following in many parts of the world. He also set up the Institute of Organic Husbandry, which presented a series of weekend courses at Goosegreen. Practical instruction was given in composting, pruning, tripoding, and silage-making while Lorna served tea with home-baked scones made from stone-ground flour. A Whole Food Society was established in 1946 to put producers in touch with consumers who wanted organic produce.

Richard de la Mare of the London publishing firm Faber and Faber, who was among many visitors to Goosegreen, persuaded Turner to write the trilogy of organic farming books published in the early '50s, *Fertility Farming, Fertility Pastures,* and *Herdsmanship.* He added the booklet *Cure Your Own Cattle* to his literary output.

At about this time, Lawrence D. Hills started writing for *The Farmer.* His great mission was to establish comfrey as a major contribution to the postwar effort to feed the world. Using the Bocking strain that he had developed, he established the Great Comfrey Race in 1954. Russian Comfrey, introduced to the U.K. in the 1870s by Henry Doubleday, a Quaker smallholder, was believed to be a valuable source of protein and animal fodder. A number of farmers and horticulturalists competed for the record yields, and Lawrence D. Hills reported on their progress in the magazine *The Farmer.*

Again, F. Newman Turner led the field, growing 23 tons of comfrey per acre at Ferne Farm, Shaftesbury, Dorset, to which the family had moved in 1953. In 1958 Lawrence Hills founded the Henry Doubleday Research Association, now named Garden Organic, and invited Turner to serve as its first president.

NATURAL HEALTH FOR MAN & BEAST

Many cattlemen knew of Turner's considerable experience with the natural treatment of animals . . . and he often treated their ailing cows successfully when conventional treatments had failed. Owners asked, "My cow did so well; can you suggest anything for a problem of my own?" So Turner decided to qualify as a medical herbalist and naturopath. The farming phase of his career came to an end, and the family moved to Letchworth Garden City in Hertfordshire, about an hour outside London. Although *The Farmer* closed down, Turner continued to publish its subsection, *The Gardener,* as a monthly magazine. It was probably the first exclusively organic gardening periodical. He also edited and published *Fitness and Health from Herbs,* the magazine of the U.K.'s National Institute of Medical Herbalists.

Although he was a committed pacifist, Frank Newman Turner showed no reticence in communicating his belief that both animal and human health demanded respect for and cooperation with nature. Such ideals were at loggerheads with the powerful agrochemical and pharmaceutical industries, and Turner was no stranger to controversy. In the early 1950s, at the height of the Foot and Mouth Disease epidemic, he challenged the Ministry of Agriculture to allow him to take infected animals into his herd to prove the immunity of naturally reared stock. They refused, of course, preferring to pursue the expensive slaughter policies which still continue in the Foot and Mouth and BSE crises of our day.

His innate pugnacity, the stresses inherent in his various enterprises, not least the problems of publishing on a shoestring, and what turned out to be a genetic predisposition to heart disease, proved a lethal combination. In June 1964, while visiting herbal medicine suppliers in Germany, Turner died suddenly of a coronary thrombosis. He was 50 years old. Frank Newman Turner was one of a small band of visionaries who laid the foundations for the modern environmental revolution. He always maintained that health began in the soil, and this message continues to be carried most effectively from the grassroots — the small-scale farmers and horticulturalists who uphold organic principles. The increasing awareness of mankind's duty to nature would have delighted him.

ROGER NEWMAN TURNER, B.AC., N.D., D.O.
Letchworth Garden City, England

Roger Newman Turner, the eldest of F. Newman Turner's three sons, is a practicing naturopath, osteopath and acupuncturist. He speaks and writes on complementary and alternative therapies for human health.

FERTILITY PASTURES

Herbal leys as the basis of
soil fertility and animal health

by

NEWMAN TURNER

Praise for *Fertility Pastures*

" . . . a book that no really progressive farmer should miss."
— *Scotsman*

" . . . a book full of original thinking
by a practical farmer who has made a
success of carrying out his own ideas
. . . can be confidently recommended
to anyone who is trying to use his
pastures as well as he can."
— *Agriculture*

FOR MY WIFE

whose care and affection in providing
my 'pastures', make possible everything
I do in growing the pastures for my cattle

Acknowledgements

Howard much original work a book may describe, no writer can claim sole authorship. Many people have contributed to the effort which has produced this book.

My cows have demonstrated with unerring judgement the herbs which are essential to healthy production and the soil has responded in a remarkable way to the deep roots and mineral- rich leaves of the herbs. These are the basic facts of the whole story.

In bringing that story to book form, I have been specially grateful to my wife, for her patience and inspiration; to my secretary, Rae Thompson, for coping with every kind of task with never a thought of trade union hours; to Lucy Johnson for typing most of the manuscript; to John Newman for relieving me of the daily duties of herdsmanship and Lawrence D. Hills for many valuable suggestions and contributions in nursing the book into print. In the tiresome task of proof-reading the pen of my friend Peter D. Turner has saved me much toil.

I am ever indebted to Richard de la Mare and his colleagues of Faber and Faber Ltd., for the encouragement and understanding without which no farmer, especially this one, could ever sustain the effort needed to record his experiences in book form.

April 1955   F. NEWMAN TURNER

Contents

Illustrations

ILLUSTRATIONS

Plates 1, 2, 18, 19, 24, 28, 30, 31, 32, 33, 34, and 35
are by Douglas Allen of Bridgwater; all other Photographs
are by the Author.

Next in importance to the Divine profusion of water, light and air—these three great physical facts which render existence possible—may be reckoned the universal beneficence of grass.

Grass is the most widely distributed of all vegetable beings, and is at once the type of our life and the emblem of our mortality. Lying in the sunshine among the buttercups and dandelions of May, scarcely higher in intelligence than the minute tenants of that mimic wilderness, our earliest recollections are of grass; and when the fitful fever is ended and the foolish wrangle of the market and forum is closed, grass heals over the scar which our descent into the bosom of the earth has made, and the carpet of the infant becomes the blanket of the dead.

Grass is the Forgiveness of Nature—her constant benefaction. Fields trampled with battle, saturated with blood, torn with the ruts of the cannon grow green again with grass and carnage is forgotten. Streets abandoned by traffic become grass-grown, like rural lanes, and are obliterated. Forests decay, harvests perish, flowers vanish, but grass is immortal. Beleaguered by the sullen hosts of winter, it withdraws into the impregnable fortress of its subterranean vitality, and emerges upon the first solicitation of the spring. Sown by the winds, by wandering birds, propagated by the subtle horticulture of the elements which are its ministers and servants, it softens the rude outline of the world. Its tenacious fibres hold the earth in its place and prevent its soluble components from washing into the wasting sea. It invades the solitude of the deserts, climbs the inaccessible slopes and forbidding pinnacles of mountains, modifies climates, and determines the history, character and destiny of nations.

Unobtrusive and patient, it has immortal vigour and aggression. Banished from the thoroughfare and the field it bides its time to return and when vigilance is relaxed, or the dynasty has perished, it silently resumes the throne from which it has been expelled, but which it never abdicates. It bears no blazonry of bloom to charm the sense with, fragrance or splendour, but its homely hue is more enchanting than the lily or the rose. It yields no fruit in earth or air, and yet, should its harvest fail for a single year, famine would depopulate the world.

JOHN JAMES INGALLS,
'Bluegrass', *Kansas Magazine,* 1872.

CHAPTER I

Why Herbal Leys

What is fertility? Bulk feeding vindicated

One of the first farming lessons I learned in my north-country boy-hood was the value of the ley or temporary pasture in the cropping rotation. In those days it was used mainly to provide first-class seeds hay for winter feeding, and grazing for the sheep. I have since come to regard the ley, properly constituted and intelligently farmed, as the main source of food for both winter and summer for all types of cattle; and, what is more, as the best means of building fertility to supply all the require-ments of any cash crops which may follow in rotation. In other words the ley or temporary pasture can be the sole provider of food and fertility for soil and livestock. A piece of barren land left to nature sooner or later becomes a pasture, provided it starts with some means of maintaining life. Many a piece of barren land has been abandoned by man because of his inability to restore fertility. Soil is the source of all life, but soil without herbage is inert and incapable of giving life; hence the key to the life of the soil is the herbage which covers and permeates the top soil and converts the subsoil rock and mineral into vital nutriment for man and beast.

Farming is the process of utilizing the life of the soil for the maintenance of man and beast, involving the growing and removal of varying propor-tions of the living substance of the soil. Husbandry is the balancing of that process by rotational alternating periods of extraction and re-creation. The secret of good husbandry is the proper utilization of the herbage, which, in partnership with the animal, has the ability to rebuild the fertility of the most inert of soils; of converting, with the aid of air, sunlight and moisture, a barren rock into a living soil. The husbandman of to-day can imitate nature's process of soil restoration with herbage by means of the ley or temporary pasture. Nature's pasture, though a complex mixture of

1

herbage, is limited to the species and varieties which are available within bird-carrying distance. Man, on the other hand, is able to select his ingredients according to the needs of the soil and the animals which will ultimately graze the pasture. Nature's pasture, though always fertility-building for the soil, is not necessarily abundantly nutritive to the animal, for its yield is limited by the variety of grasses, clovers and herbs available in the neighbourhood, and the quality of its herbage by the treatment which is subsequently receives.

The first purpose of a natural pasture, therefore, appears to be to cover the soil, to correct the balance in the soil, and to build the fertility of the soil. The value of the pasture for grazing purposes depends almost entirely on the extent to which it is grazed, the variety of grazing which it receives, and the times of year at which it is grazed.

It almost seems that nature provides the basic coverage or pasture and leaves it to the animal to adjust the quality and value of the pasture for grazing purposes. I have seen rough grazing turned into good pasture with nothing more than good grazing management. I have also seen newly re-seeded pastures of expensive ingredients turned into poor rough grazing by bad grazing management.

The main purpose of man-made pastures has usually been to provide for his domestic animals their summer feeding requirements and a part of their winter needs. Any benefit to soil fertility in the process of providing that food has been only a secondary consideration. Soil fertility has rarely been regarded as any more than a very unimportant by-product of food production. In the majority of leys the ingredients are planned exclusively for their potential bulk yield above ground, with no thought for the underground or top-soil effect of the ingredients. Further, little or none of the product of the pasture is normally fed back to the soil directly for soil fertility purposes.

I want in this book to show the greater, indeed almost all-sufficient value, of the ley, when its soil fertility potentialities are placed first in order of importance, as in nature. I want to demonstrate how, when we make a pasture on nature's model of complex ingredients, for the primary purpose of building soil fertility, we can also achieve for the grazing animal, food of a quality which will enable the animal to maintain its own health and fertility and produce abundantly of milk and progeny.

Accepting the main purpose of the temporary pasture to be fertility in soil and animal (in that order) I must at this point define what I mean by fertility.

Fertility in the soil means to me the ability to produce abundant yields of crops which are disease-free, the seeds of which have the capacity to reproduce healthy crops and to transmit health, productive ability *and fertility* to the animal and human consumer.

This means, that in order to be considered fertile, a soil must not only yield in quantity, but a full complement in that quantity of all the essentials of a vigorous and fertile life—minerals, micro-elements, vitamins, plant hormones—the essentials of health and growth; proteins, carbo-hydrates, fats—the essentials of nutrition and live-weight increase. If any of these factors is found to be lacking in the ultimate consumer of the crop grown in a particular soil, it maybe assumed that the soil was not fully fertile.

Quality in food is the end-product of a fertile soil. All the above-mentioned essentials that such a soil must transmit to the grazing pasture, are the ingredients of quality in that pasture. Additionally, quality implies vitality or life; and for the human consumer also flavour, both of which are absent in synthetic foods, or foods which are over-stimulated during their period of growth. The word *whole* to my mind conveys the meaning which we seek in food quality: for to have quality, food must be whole in the essentials of health, life *and the power to reproduce life.*

The orthodox scientist normally measures the fertility of a soil by its *bulk* yield, with no relation to *effect* on the ultimate consumer.

I have seen cattle slowly lose condition and fall in milk yield when fed entirely on the abundant produce of an *apparently* fertile soil. Though the soil was capable of yielding heavy crops, those crops were not adequate in themselves to maintain body-weight and milk production in the cow, without supplements. That soil, though capable of above-average yields, and by the orthodox quantitative measure regarded as fertile, could not, by the more complete measure of ultimate effect on the consumer, be regarded as anything but deficient in fertility.

Fertility therefore, is the ability to produce, at the highest recognized level of yield, crops of a quality which, when consumed over long periods by animals or man, enable them to sustain health, bodily condition and high level of production without evidence of disease or deficiency of any kind.

Fertility cannot be measured quantitatively. Any measure of soil fertility must be related to the quality of its produce. The fact that sterility has resulted in animals grazing and depending entirely for their nutrition on pastures which by all orthodox quantitative measures are fully fertile, is an indication of the failure of the quantitative measure when unrelated to ultimate effect.

To put it in a few words: the most simple measure of soil fertility is its ability to transmit, through its produce, fertility to the ultimate consumer. Any breakdown or deficiency in the animal or human dependent is a measure of the infertility of the original soil from which the animal or human has derived its food.

It is evident then that just as fertility is the ability to yield food of a quality capable of transmitting fertility, so quality in food is possible only from a fertile soil.

This brings me to the conclusion that we should use our rotational pastures or leys, firstly for the purpose of building and maintaining soil fertility, secondly to provide summer grazing, and thirdly to provide food for the winter in the form of silage or hay, and a proportion of winter grazing. Experimenting over the past fifteen years, on the basis of such reasoning, I have developed a system of ley farming which provides, with the assistance of organic manuring, the sole requirements for soil fertility and the necessary replenishment of crop nutrients; which gives all the food requirements of the dairy herd for the greater part of the year. The cows help themselves to this food whether it is in grazing the ley, eating the silage from the ley, or other forage crops such as kale or oats and vetches, which, for a short time in the year, and used to assist the ley in providing the bulk of the animal's nutritional needs.

The reason that I came to regard the ley as the main provider of food for my cattle during those years, was the belief, which arose from my study of animal diseases, that these diseases are mostly caused by our manner of feeding our cattle. I came to the conclusion that all animal disease had its real foundation in the toxic condition of the animal body, brought about by unnatural methods of management and in particular the method of feeding. I found that even homegrown foods, when forced with chemical fertilizers, could not keep my animals in health. Orthodox feeding of dairy cattle had as its primary aim the stimulation of maximum milk yield, with little or no regard for the health of the cow, and hardly any means in the dietary of assuring the health essentials which are contained in fresh food grown in naturally-manured, humus-rich soil. These factors, which the nutritionists have failed to isolate, are nevertheless available from fresh-growing forage crops in a form which cannot be provided in manufactured compound foods. We are learning more and more of the value of minor elements in nutrition and health maintenance, which have until recently been disregarded by the scientist or were unknown to him. Plant hormones, for instance, are no doubt a potent factor in the development of essential hormone secretions in the animal body, yet hormones cannot be substituted artificially through the plant to the animal in the way they unquestionably are when the animal grazes a ley or forage crop with its roots still in the earth. Under modern methods of feeding the dairy cow, the higher the yield of the cow the less natural food is she allowed to have. The greater her potentiality for milk production the lower her intake of the foods which are rich in the natural essentials of health.

In 1943 I wrote the following: 'Health goes in at the mouth, and if we cut down the health-giving foods provided by Nature to function in ways that we cannot fully understand, all the veterinary surgeons in the world will not save our cows from a doom which commercialized (i.e. commercially controlled) science is designing for them . . . my cows must be given their food as far as possible while it still has its roots in Mother Earth. And, in the degree which natural feeding is not possible, I must provide the widest possible variety of herbs as sources of the mineral and trace elements essential to health.'

Herbal pastures of three to five years' duration have proved to be the complete answer to my requirements in the provision of soil fertility and health-giving animal nutrition. The herbal ley is my manure merchant, my food manufacturer and my vet, all in one; and, what is more to the point for the working farmer, it produces an average of eight to nine hundred gallons of milk each from Jersey cows at a cost which would put all three of these friends of the orthodox farmer completely out of business if they were compelled to cut their charges to the same rate as it costs to feed *my* cows and keep them in health by means of the herbal ley.

*　*　*

It is just about eleven years since I first considered my cattle-feeding and management methods sufficiently successful to justify publishing them. In spite of the depression through which the Boutflour system of 'cut-the-bulk-increase-the concentrates' was passing, owing to the rationing of concentrates, I got little or no encouragement from the experts.

The orthodox farming press had no space for my ideas; the advocacy of natural home-grown bulky food and the natural prevention and treatment of disease, enticed no advertisement revenue. And though cattle-cake advertisers could at that time do little more than prestige advertising, it was safe to assume that the war would end one day, and the full-page adverts of cattle foods and supplements would once more proclaim disease and death to the cow and increasing profits to the food processors and mass-circulation publishers.

The cash-controlled farm gates were closed not only to my revolutionary methods—but even to the non-advertisement-revenue-earning, yet obviously beneficial, ideas of others.

Tripod haymaking, which we featured in several issues of *The Farmer* in 1946 and 1947, describing my, and other organic farmers', successful use of the system in previous years, was spurned as impracticable. The late Captain Alexander Proctor, who I am glad to say lived just long enough to see official acceptance of his system, was with no encouragement from the experts or the orthodox press, having an uphill struggle to persuade farmers to try this foolproof system of 'weatherproof haymaking' (the description which I suggested to him and which has since been widely adopted). He was not a potential large advertiser and relied on personal recommendations from one farmer to another and the hard work of some fellow enthusiasts. I wrote and distributed 20,000 copies of a pamphlet called *Weatherproof Harvesting* [Publisher's note: This pamphlet is included as a chapter in the book *Fertility Farming*], which has, no doubt, over the past seven or eight years, helped towards the present-day acceptance of this system as the only effective way of making good-quality, high-protein hay; its enthusiastic use by the director of a Ministry of Agriculture Experimental Farm; the commencement of national advertising by the manufacturers of tripods; and, at last, featuring of the system in the national farming press—or at least the braver section of it.

But tripod haymaking was always just a common-sense way of doing a particular job of work on the farm. I tell this short story of my early advocacy of it, merely to illustrate the slow acceptance of even the simplest farming improvements when the loud fanfares of high finance are not available to move the mass-circulation journals out of their mercenary rut.

So it is a matter of great satisfaction to me that, after only eleven years of preaching reliance on home-grown forage as the most economical way to healthy milk production; the breeding of cattle capable of converting natural foods; the avoidance of high protein stimulation as a safeguard against diseases, and exploding the myth of excessive yields obtained at high cost in food and health; that some or all of these ideas (which were without a kind word in official circles and orthodox press when I first advocated them) are now finding favour and successful practice by a number of leading authorities, and, what is even more gratifying, gaining publicity in the orthodox farming press.

An article of mine published in June 1944, said: 'It is surely better farming to keep two 750-gallon cows, producing milk at a cost of 1s. a gallon, than one 1,500-gallon cow producing milk at a cost of 1s. 6d. a gallon. The difference in profit on milk alone would be considerable, to say nothing of the value of the extra calf in a pedigree herd. In other words what matters is not so much how much milk a cow gives but the cost in cash and disease of producing each gallon of milk.'

In 1945, summarizing the methods I had found successful in developing a disease-free low-cost milk-producing herd, I wrote the following, which was published in Soil and Health and later enlarged upon in *Fertility Farming*.

Thus I reached my conclusions regarding the real causes of disease in cattle, which I summarize as follows:

'Artificial feeding with concentrated foods which lack the health factors of fresh whole foods. Scientific feeding of dairy cattle has as its primary aim the stimulation of maximum milk yield with little consideration for the health of the cow, with no means of assuring the provision of those health essentials which are contained in fresh food grown in naturally manured, humus-rich soil, and which the nutritionist has so far failed to isolate and prepare artificially for inclusion in manufactured compound foods.

'What are the main differences, that our herds should contain so much more disease to-day than they did in my father's and grandfather's day? Intensified exploitation of the dairy cow, artificial feeding, and the mad race for higher and higher yields with all the attendant artificial practices which have multiplied as disease has become more widespread. . . .

'I must provide adequately of all the bulky natural foods before considering concentrated feeding; kale, silage, hay and straw must come before cake.'

Now in 1954 in articles in *The Dairy Farmer,* based on a development of my natural bulk-feeding methods, Mr. Stephen Williams, Farm Director of Boots' Farms in Nottinghamshire, starts with the heading: 'This 4 lb. per gallon cut-down-the-bulk system is *wrong!*' and says:

'Every dairy farmer who has adopted feeding according to yield and bulk control will admit, if he is honest, that although maybe he gets a few higher yields, his costs per gallon rise and so does his vet's bill.

'And the higher the yields go beyond a certain average, the more the food and veterinary expenses rise.

'Thus many farmers are building a form of dairy farming in which the average life of a biggish dairy cow goes something like this: first calf, 1,000 to 1,200 gallons; second calf, the same again; third calf, no more than 1,000 gallons—then out, through disease, disaster or death.'

Disadvantages of the orthodox system are given as follows:

'The cow is given increasing amounts of concentrated food and less bulk, despite the fact that she is designed to consume high-quality roughage foods.

'She is deliberately steamed up in a short period before calving just when her hormone system is diverting food to udder and mammary development; consequently the development is overdone.

'At her peak yield, when body metabolism is working at its hardest and is acutely responsive to any upset, she is overloaded with concentrates with which she is not fitted to deal and underfed with food appropriate to her digestive system.

'She is denied the benefit of being reduced to a nice breeding condition once a year.

'Through being forced for a high peak yield she develops a hock-slapping bag subject to easy injury and bad for machine milking.

'She is denied the opportunity of developing capacity—without which she cannot achieve maximum efficiency in using quality roughage foods.'

He goes on in his second article to describe his system:

'It is a very simple system. It involves allowing a cow to eat all the high-quality roughage food she will eat, whether she is at peak yield, at low yield, or dry. And she also gets a fairly level amount of concentrates—from 4 to 12 or 14 lb. a day.

'Of course, this sounds odd after years of propaganda for feeding according to yield and controlling bulk. But it is far from odd when it is examined in the light of modern knowledge.

'To begin with, scientific research is producing more and more evidence every day to prove to us what we all really know and what we seem to have forgotten—that a cow is a ruminating animal with a digestive apparatus designed to extract the nutrients she requires from fibrous foods.'

Also pursuing my system of natural feeding, Mr. J. R. Stubbs started another series of articles on 'forage' farming and said:

'It is a system by which farmers can make the greatest possible use of cheaply produced, high quality, labour-saving *grazed* crops.

'What is more, despite the fact that milk sales per cow may only average 700 to 750 gallons on forage farming, the milk yield per acre is substantially increased simply because forage production per acre is so high that stocking rates can be much heavier.

'And as we are limited in acres but not number of cows, clearly the acre must be the unit of ultimate importance.

'This is a new way to look at dairy farming. The old way was to increase total income by feeding expensive foods to get more milk per cow. It succeeded—but at less profit per gallon.

'The new way is to increase milk yields per acre by carrying more stock on cheaper foods and so increase the margin between cost of production and selling price that farm income can be raised even if the price of milk is lowered.

'The system offers other benefits to commend it. Because the cows do most of their own food carting, the labour costs of cow management are reduced. Because the cows do their own dung spreading, labour costs are still further reduced. Cow-hours cost very little; man-hours cost 3s. each.

'The evidence we have so far also suggests that the health of animals is better under forage farming than under traditional methods, that they live longer and produce better; they get into exceptionally good condition during their dry periods and there are fewer breeding problems.

'When cows have access to forage crops at the right stage of growth, milk yields are then better maintained during the normally difficult months of July, November and January than they are when concentrates are fed as the main milk-producing foods.'

In *The Farmers' Weekly* recently, Rex Paterson wrote a detailed article asking the question: 'Do we want these High Yields?', and concluding that at the present cost of concentrated feeding-stuffs they are no longer a proposition. He, too, advocated reasonable yields on bulky home-grown foods as the common-sense course. He said: 'It is high time to question whether high yield per cow is really a measure of efficiency and to consider yields in terms of milk per acre.'

Professor Cooper of Wye College, among many others, is preaching the value of leys as the most economical food for the milking cow: in winter as silage or hay and in summer for grazing.

And when the Chief Agricultural Adviser to the Ministry of Agriculture, Sir James Scott Watson, says that the time has come when we must consider costs in relation to higher yields (of crops this time), we *are* getting somewhere.

Read this extract from the report of an interview he gave to *The Farmers' Weekly:*

'Although Sir James believes that still higher yields can be achieved, he views the future with his feet firmly planted on the ground. There is a risk, he pointed out, that we may forget our old experience and jump into exploiting scientific discoveries a little too eagerly at times.

'If you take the farming of the eastern counties, nobody would suggest a return to the old four-course rotation, but it is rather a big change from that to barley, after barley after barley.

'If you use MCPA instead of fallow crops, it does not necessarily mean that that is the complete answer—because there are winter stock, muck and other things to consider.

'Specialization is still bringing us difficulties with soil-borne diseases. Potato eelworm is the outstanding example. We are worried, too, about cereal root eelworm, which seems to be spreading. Take-all and eyespot have taken a pretty heavy toll on some farms in recent years.'

CHAPTER II

The Complete Diet for Cattle

Just as the feeding of the soil has been concentrated on purely chemical needs and the measurement of soil nutrition has stopped at N.P. and K., so the feeding of farm animals has been limited to the provision of starch equivalent and protein equivalent. In recent years *some* attention *has* been given to mineral needs in animal nutrition and some vague acknowledgment of trace elements is now accepted. But these latter developments have been based mainly on the commercial possibilities of *synthetic* mineral supplements. No organized attempt has been made to investigate ways of ensuring the complete nutrition of the animal through the growing crop.

The whole point of my practice and advocacy of natural or bulk feeding (roughage or forage feeding are alternative descriptions of the system) is the sheer necessity of such a system of feeding to the *complete* nutrition and health of the animal.

Starch equivalent and protein equivalent fed in at one end of a cow *will* produce milk at the other end. But the man who discovered this fact forgot about the cow in the middle, between the starch and protein equivalent and the milk. He forgot that she too has to operate a complex and delicate system which processes the starch equivalent and protein equivalent into milk; to build a young animal inside her, and to maintain her own health. None of these things are automatic unless nutrition is complete to the last minute trace of some obscure element, or a tiny proportion of one of a long list of vitamins or many other prerequisites of glandular or bacterial functioning in the animal system, about which official research has hardly begun to consider.

Take the simple example of vitamins. Human health is considered impossible without an adequate supply of vitamins. We are advised to take vitamin pills in the winter when our summer sun has been inadequate, or the amount of fresh fruit and vegetables may be small. If we don't get enough vitamins from food or sun, these vitamin supplements are considered essential to continuing health. Yet the poor old cow is asked to produce, from her bodily reserves, a calf and a thousand gallons of milk without a thought for her vitamin needs, on a diet which her stomachs were never designed to digest—and which in consequence calls for a complete reorganization of her digestive processes.

The ruminant stomachs were designed to deal with coarse roughage. Nothing more concentrated than spring grass and its natural admixture of herbs was ever intended to pass to the inside of a cow. And nature provided in the stomach and intestines a group of bacteria whose task it was to break down this fibrous food into the requirements of lactation and pregnancy.

The continued passage of this natural food through the stomachs and alimentary canal, fostered and at the same time encouraged the right bacterial flora. The vitamins, in which such a diet was rich, maintained a healthy and vigorous system; and the plant hormones present in fresh whole food—the precursors of glandular functions in the body—maintained the harmony and balanced functioning of all the organs of the animal system.

In addition to the vitamins and hormones in right proportions and adequate quantities, the deep roots of the natural herbage of the woodlands, fields and hedgerows, tapped the soil at all levels from the top soil to many feet down in the subsoil and rock, to provide a vast complex of minerals and trace elements, all of which, in however microscopic a quantity, are imperative parts of perfect metabolism and complete nutrition.

It is obvious then, that any efficient attempt to maintain the animal in health, *as well as* profitable production, must provide all these essentials of complete nutrition, and probably many other factors still not discovered or isolated from the natural diet. No man would suggest to-day that we know everything that exists in the complete diet of the animal. It is in the lifetime of most adult readers of this book that three of the most important factors in the diet of human or animal were discovered. Fifty years ago it was believed that carbohydrates, proteins and fats were the only constituents of our food; and animal nutrition has rested ever since on those requirements (with vague suggestions for the addition of synthetic minerals). But who would be bold enough, even now that we have discovered vitamins, trace-elements, hormones, digestive enzymes and bacteria, to suggest that nothing remains to be discovered about the science of nutrition?

And since no mere man can *begin* accurately to estimate the correct ratio or relationship in which the animal needs, or can assimilate, all these *known* essentials, let alone the still undiscovered elements or organisms, there is only one way of ensuring *complete* nutrition; and that is to provide the bulk of the diet in natural form.

I believe the herbal ley comes as near as it is possible to get to the natural diet, in a form which produces maximum milk or meat production from every acre while at the same time maintaining health and low production costs.

In addition to providing what I believe to be the perfect basic diet for economical and healthful milk production, it does it at a lower cost in labour and machinery for both harvesting and feeding it, than any other system I know. And, what is more, once the ley is established and is available for grazing or cutting for silage, it provides the most foolproof system of feeding that can be devised. No exact measurement of starch equivalent and protein equivalent, or pounds per gallon, or maintenance and production ration, is necessary. The orthodox books on animal nutrition, certainly the sections of them referring to cows, may be forgotten. With the publication of *Fertility Pastures* I believe that they are out of date. The high costs for purchased feeding-stuffs, the balancing of home-grown production rations, the labour of feeding them to housed cattle and adjusting the varying proportions of concentrates, hay, silage and/or roots, can no longer be tolerated, at present milk prices, by the farmer who farms for a living. Let the hobby farmer continue mopping up his business profits—though there are easier ways of doing even that than carrying food to cows which have twice as many legs as the man who carries her food. There is little scope for cutting costs, except in the cost of feeding: for labour costs are more likely to rise than fall, and there is a limit, which is very nearly reached in the most progressive herds, to the forcing of the cow to ever higher and higher yields. The suggestion by the on-to-the-3,000-gallon-herd-average boys, that there is no limit to the amount of milk a cow can be bred and fed to yield, will not be accepted by intelligent farmers, unless their striving for the carrot dangling before them causes them to miss the opportunities of profitable milk production by natural methods, which this book lays at their feet.

My feeding methods, then, are simply to allow the cow to help herself to as much as she wants of well-controlled herbal leys in the months of March or April till October or November; and for the months of November to March to allow her as much as she cares to take of silage made from the same leys. In addition we allow some kale, controlled by electric fence, to be grazed in the winter months; and a handful or two of ground dredge corn to be given to the higher yielding cows during milking. Some good oat straw was provided, as litter around the silage heap and in the lie-back pasture to raise the dry roughage content of the diet and assist cudding, in our first year of all-silage feeding; but last winter, after a harvest which left us short of good feeding straw, we fed none, and the cows did, if anything, rather better on silage and kale only.

Provision needs to be made each year for about 6-8 tons of silage per cow according to breed, 10 cwt. of dredge corn (mixed cereals and pulses), and $\frac{1}{4}$ acre of late-sown leafy kale for each cow which is to be in milk in the winter period. The dredge corn is not an *essential*—a 750 gallon herd average (with Jerseys) can be maintained entirely on silage and grass. While we need to use a little straw we also grow a little dredge corn, and feeding the ground dredge corn will maintain an 850-950 gallon herd average.

For summer grazing on the good, well-managed ley, approximately 1 acre per cow should be needed. Last year my herd of Jerseys was unable to keep down half an acre for each cow. If the soil is not so good and the ley is not likely to achieve maximum production, start with $1\frac{1}{2}$ acres of ley for each cow and use the surplus for silage. The grazing acreage can always be reduced as fertility builds up and the yield of the ley increases.

CHAPTER III

Self-service Silage and Kale

The only really valid argument I have met against my advocacy of natural feeding of cattle with high-quality roughage has been that of labour costs. Though I believe it reasonable to argue that it is better to *grow* foodstuffs than to buy them in these days of mechanized harvesting, no one has yet mechanized the *feeding* of silage, hay, and kale, and *I* am certainly not mechanically-minded enough to devise any machine that can, for instance, cut silage in the heap and fork it into the cows' manger or even spread it in the field. I have often thought it ought to be possible to adapt the manure loader and spreader to get silage out of the heap or pit and spread it in the field; but no one has yet done it that I know of, so for most of us who believe in bulk feeding of roughage the hard labour and its very high cost have continued.

There is no profit in cash gained by replacing bought concentrates only to pay it out on extra labour; the key to profitable milk production is the growing of better winter keep than you can buy, better for both your pocket and your cattle.

Growing-grass is a much more effective food grazed, than eaten after any known system of conservation. Just as milk is more valuable to the calf when it is suckled direct from the dam, grasses and herbs, or any green crop is more valuable eaten fresh from the soil.

I have found, then, that winter grazing of kale and other crops is not only more nutritious and health-giving to the animal, but more economical to the farmer. And pursuing this principle of reducing the greatest cost in winter feeding—labour—I have found that it is possible for the cow to help herself to *all* the winter food she needs. This applies not only to the grazing of kale but to the feeding of silage and hay (though of the latter I feed only a little, and that only to calves). My cows now help themselves to everything except the bit of dredge corn which they have while being milked.

My winter feeding system combines the self-feeding of kale and silage and also hay when this is used, all at the same time. The cow merely helps herself to either one or two or all of them as she needs them. My policy has for many years been to allow these bulky foods almost *ad lib.*, to the exclusion or severe limitation of concentrates. But until I devised my combination self-feeding system it has involved a tremendous lot of labour—cutting the kale and silage and carrying it to the cows. Now this labour is completely eliminated. Apart from the winter-born calves which are indoors in the winter, work with the cattle amounts to little more than milking them. The long hours of winter feeding have now been reduced to summer proportions. Even when the cows were yarded at night we have racks which hold a week's supply of silage and oat straw so that no food need be carried to the yarded cattle more often than once a week.

Last winter we made and fed 400 tons of silage at a total cost of only 10s. a ton, and ten acres of kale which cost a total of £57 10s. to grow, and £10 to strip graze. Additionally only 5 tons of a dredge corn mixture were used for 'production ration,' at a value of £125 total (at market prices), making, with the addition of wages absorbed by milk production, our winter milk costs only 1s. 3d. per gallon, which included also the cost of feeding all young stock, which after all are part of our milk-production costs. I hesitate to quote this figure for fear it is used as a basis for further cutting the price of milk at the next February price review—but it is only by such drastic cost-cutting that we shall survive as food producers, for milk prices are going down whatever we farmers may say or do. And even heavy fertilizer applications, in an attempt to combat falling prices with increased yields, are now in most cases only at great ultimate cost in soil fertility and merely delay the doom!

Such a low cost of milk production is made possible by ruthless slashing of the two major items of cost in milk production —feeding-stuffs and labour. The saving in labour achieved by the self-service system of silage and kale feeding means that in mid-winter, while milk prices are highest, we have continued summer-grass milk-production costs. The farmer's dream of perpetual summer-grass on to which the cows are turned to get their fill, to return to fill the pail, is now all but a practical reality. The main cost of our winter milk production is making the silage in the summer; and thanks to Mr. Rex Patterson's buckrake and our own careful simplification of the system of making high quality silage without frills, even that item of cost is infinitesimal.

Though silage is at last being accepted as an essential part of low-cost milk production, it has been rather because of the lash of incessant rain

1. Mowing an herbal ley ready for silage-making. This is the stage of growth, just before flowering of herbs and grasses at which maximum nutritional value per acre is obtained.

2. Buck-raking the above pasture for silage.

3. Commencing the silage heap.

4. Compressing the heap.

than the love of silage as a fodder. British weather has driven the dairy farmer to this system of grass conservation reluctantly. If it weren't for the capital outlay he would probably prefer to make dried grass even though the finished product is, in my experience, a much less valuable food.

This reluctance to make silage results from the very involved and cumbersome methods which have been propagated by commercial interests with concrete silos, cutter-blowers, earthscoops, and various acids and chemicals to sell. No wonder most farmers have considered modern silage-making a costly and laborious way of spoiling good grass. For as often as not these involved aids to silage-making have only enabled the farmer to turn lush clover into inedible manure, the smell of which has caused many a fireside threat of a broken home from a wife whose Parfum d'amour has nothing on the old man's silage-scented breeches steaming beside a roaring fire on a frosty evening!

I am not suggesting that good silage cannot be made in tower silos or even expensively excavated pits, with a £1,000 cutter-chopper-pick-up, or cutter-blower-upper. Of course it can; but at what cost, not only in the making—but in the sweat and toil of cutting out of the pit or silo and carting it to the cows. I don't know how you feel; but though I don't mind a good sweat every day in midsummer when I can throw off everything except my hairy chest, I have no enthusiasm for sweating in a silage pit before spreading the silage for the heifers on the hillside in driving sleet.

All the joy goes out of the very best silage when these points are considered; and what you may consider perfect silage, regardless of cost, becomes a failure if it has to be dug out of a pit and carted to the cows. So it is well worth learning how to do the job in the quickest way with a minimum of labour, machinery and unnecessary wear and tear on tyres and gumboots. That means to make it where the cows can eat it, digest it, and spread the fertility from it; while all you have to do is to call them in to be milked and collect the top winter prices at summer costs.

Textbooks, including sections describing how silage should be made, are numerous—but I've yet to read the book saying how it is made by the man who makes it and feeds it cheaply; so I'll attempt to describe my method, if only for the reason that it is the cheapest and easiest method of conserving summer grass and keeping it at its optimum nutritional health-giving and production value that I know.

In making the silage in the field, water to moisten the grass is not always practicable, and molasses, to sweeten it and set in motion desirable ferments, needs water to dilute it. So, for our field self-service silage clamps, we use neither water nor molasses, nor, of course, any of the recommended acids, salts or other activators.

The site of the heap varies from year to year, so there can be no question of concrete sides or base. And though straw bales might be possible, we don't use them because they make no difference to the amount of waste on the sides of the heap. Waste at top and sides depends entirely on the amount of compression in relation to the maturity of the crop. The coarser or more mature the crop that is being used, the greater the amount of compression needed to avoid side and top wastage. It is possible by the open-sided system to have no waste on the sides if it is built at the sides as carefully as the old stack builders built their haystacks; whereas with concrete or straw-bale walls, the silage always shrinks inwards from them, and moist air between wall and silage, which can never dry, causes decomposition.

Siting of the heap depends on the relationship of the kale crop if it is to be self-fed in conjunction with strip-grazed kale; but ideally it should not be in a corner. The site of the silage heap will become the most fertile area of the field, with fertility radiating from it in diminishing quality. This concentration of fertility ought therefore to be on the poorest portion of the field.

The fertility-building value of a self-service silage clamp is one of those free gifts which comes from thoughtful farming. Compare the cost of getting the same fertility into the field if you cut the silage, cart it to the silo or silage pit in or near the farmyard, feed the silage in the buildings or yard, and carry the manure to the field again to be spread by hand or even tractor-driven manure spreader. How much easier to make and feed the silage on the field where it grows, and to allow the cows to provide the labour and motive power to spread their own manure back to the field that provided it.

In climates where it is possible to milk in the field in winter, this system brings to perfection Mr. Hosier's outdoor bale milking system.

So the heap is sited in a spot from which fertility may radiate, provided easy access to the kale is also possible. I have elaborated in Chapter V the possibilities of this arrangement in building fertility on worn-out land, and maintaining it by a three-course rotation, where, on the same field, it is possible to provide entirely for the cows of grass, silage, kale and corn, building up a vast store of fertility as the corn follows the grazed kale and self-feed silage with its aftermath of self-spread dung. (See Chapter V, *Self-feeding for the Soil.*)

One final point about the site of the silage heap, which may not be thought of until you have, like me, had to shovel a snowdrift off the silage heap while a sleet-laden gale slices the lobes of your ears! Choose a sheltered spot; for neither cows nor cowman will rejoice in self-service silage under a snowdrift or in the face of a fierce nor'easter. One heap we sited on the wrong side of a hedge produced some wonderful silage; yet in the very worst weather the cows preferred empty stomachs and shelter rather than walk round the corner to eat silage in a snowstorm.

In building the heap the important man is the one (or more) on the heap. It is easy enough to sweep the grass up from the swathe with a buckrake and carry it to the site of the heap, dump it and run over it a few times with the tractor. But the man on the heap has to tease out the lumps of green crop which would cause air pockets to form and decay or mould to fill them during the settling of the heap. He it is who decides where each buckrake load should be dropped in order to keep the material level and evenly compressed, and he should see that the tractors have passed backward and forward over the heap a sufficient number of times between each layer to ensure adequate compression. But above all he must himself trample tightly the extreme sides of the heap, where it is too perilous for the tractor wheels to pass.

Whenever possible he should occupy the outer edge of the heap while standing to tease out the grass, and frequent trampling up and over the outer sides of the heap are necessary to avoid leaving the sides too springy and loose. All the men on the job should join in this march along the sides at the end of each session at the heap, if waste along the outsides of the heap is to be minimized. Keep the top of the heap flat. If the middle is higher during building than the outside it will result in a poorer compaction of the outer edges.

The right time at which to cut the green crop in order to achieve maximum production from the cows which eat the ultimate silage, is a matter of stage of growth of the crop and month of the year. Theoretically, the *stage* at which the leaf protein is at its highest is the right one at which to cut, whether the month is May or September. This, in my experience, is just a little too soon for best results. At the stage of highest protein the crop has too high a moisture content to make good silage and much of the value of the grass leaches out from the heap. Protein is not the only criterion in maximum milk production, and even in mid-winter is not necessarily the most important to the cow, as many high-yield advocates believe; though I do recognize the importance of getting as much protein as possible from the silage especially in this method of natural feeding. But the juices which are lost in making silage from too young a growth contain vitamins and digestive enzymes, and I believe some of the yet immeasurable essentials of healthy and abundant production. So I find the ideal stage to cut the crop is just after what the experts consider to be the highest protein stage: that is, just before the grasses flower. At this stage the ley may be cut and carried straight to the silage heap—with no need to wilt it to reduce its moisture content, and no need to add water to raise the moisture content (as would be advisable if the crop is left too long).

And as regards the best month of the year to cut for silage: well, if the growth has reached the ideal mowing stage described above in the months of May or June, that is when the best silage can be made. But just as the importance of protein has been over-exaggerated so has the month of the year. A fertile soil will produce nearly as good a silage in August and early September so far as its milk- or beef-yielding capabilities are concerned, though it is probable that the natural *growth* impulse of springtime in the early-summer silage may have some special health virtues, the value of which we cannot yet measure.

Our first effort at self-feeding silage was from a surface wedge-shaped clamp. This was made in the field where it was intended to winter the cattle, and if it could also be the field in which the silage crop grew so much the better. This meant that for preference our silage was made from an established ley, which would carry cattle in the winter without serious poaching, or from one due to be broken and cropped again in the following spring, so that poaching does not matter. Alternatively, we take an arable silage crop of oats and vetches from a field immediately adjacent to an old pasture or established ley, so that the cows may help themselves to the silage and lie back on to the pasture.

The wedge-shaped clamp was made above ground-level with a sloping ramp up to a vertical end.

The crop is mown in the late evening of the day before it is to be carried—or the early morning of the same day—enough to keep (in our case) two buck-rakes going for the day. The green crop is dropped by the buck-rake on the site chosen for the clamp teased out and levelled by hand labour and the tractor runs over it to compress it. A sloping run-up for the tractor is kept on one end and the other end is built up vertically like the side of a haystack.

This results in a great depth of first-class silage with practically no waste, except at ground-level at the foot of the ramp, and is probably the least wasteful of all systems of silage making.

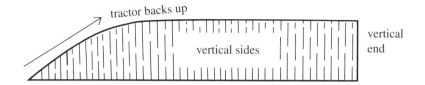

But the wedge clamp has two serious disadvantages. The first is the danger of a foot slipping and the tractor going back over the end. This happened on a farm near me and the tractor-driver was pinned under the tractor with a broken neck. One of my own men drove over the side by allowing his foot to slip off the clutch when too near the edge; and though he was able to jump to safety the tractor toppled over and went up in flames. The second disadvantage is that with the vertical-ended clamp the area of the self-feeding table available for the cattle is limited—and one end is too high for them to feed from at all.

One of the accepted principles of silage making is that the smaller the area of exposed space in ratio to the cubic capacity of the heap the lower the percentage of waste, so that the higher the heap, the better. But for self-feeding there is a limit to the height of the heap, if the cattle are to be able to help themselves at all times. The settled height of the heap must not be more than the cow can comfortably reach from ground-level. If the height of the heap during making does not exceed 8-10 feet it should settle down to about 6 feet high when finished, which is the limit from which a cow can help herself. And this height-limit means that the heap must either be longer or wider. The greater the length of the heap, the greater the footage of silage from which each cow can eat.

So now we make a shallower, longer mound, still with vertical sides, but a sloping ramp at each end. There is slightly more waste at ground-level each end; but the removal of the cliff-end over which the tractor-driver can dive, and the ability to self-feed from both sides and ends, makes this the most efficient method.

The silage clamp is made above ground-level on the surface of the field, rather like a long stack with vertical sides but with a sloping ramp up either end. With grass, as with oats and vetches, it is mown in the evening of the day before it is to be carried—or the early morning of the same day—cutting enough to keep two buckrakes going for the day. The buckrake

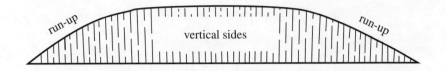

run-up   vertical sides   run-up

sweeps up the green crop from the swathe, carries it to the site chosen for the clamp, and drops it: the tractor runs right over it to compress it. We make the heap not less than two tractor widths—about 15 feet wide which enables us to get best compression. As the heap rises and lengthens, the sloping ends allow the tractor to run with its buckrake of green crop up on end, drop its load, then run down the other end. Each layer is spread by the man on the heap, then the tractor runs backwards and forwards over the heap to compress it. After the first day's work the heap is allowed to heat until it is uncomfortable to the hand, before further material is added; then we work away at it every day.

GROWING THE KALE

Kale is grown at one end of the pasture upon which the cows are to be wintered, as near as possible to the silage heap from which they are to help themselves, or alternatively in an adjacent field so that the cows may have access to both kale and silage at the same time.

In order to avoid the need to hoe the kale, to get a leafy high-protein crop instead of thick stems and to avoid the fly, we sow the kale in June or July. This also means that adjoining the arable silage heap the kale can occupy the ground from which the oat and vetch crop was cut for silage. This ground should in any case be clean following the weed-smothering effect of the vetches.

Where the kale is taken on an old arable field or a newly broken pasture, we spend as much of the spring and early summer as possible cleaning the land in readiness for the kale. This is done by the repeated use of the disc harrow or rotavator. We then sow the kale—always Thousand-headed which is leafier, more winter-hardy, and of greater feeding value than Marrowstem kale—with the grain drill, at the rate of 5 lb. an acre. This sows in rows approximately 7 in. apart. If we have been able, before sowing, to get the land sufficiently free of weeds, no further work need be done on the kale once it is sown; but if it proves that weeds are still present in numbers or varieties strong enough to compete with the kale, we knock out alternate rows with the 10-in. wide rotary hoe. Normally, however, no work need be done and, with strip grazing to solve the winter-feeding labour costs, kale grown and used in this way becomes a serious competitor with buckrake-built, self-fed silage for the cheapest winter feed for milk production.

Kale and silage fed together—with practically no labour costs—bring the cost of winter milk production just about as low as we are ever likely to get it. The one essential necessary to make these low costs doubly rewarding is to see that the silage is really first-class quality, so that it maintains a high milk yield without the additional cost of concentrates.

THE PROCEDURE FOR SELF-FEEDING

The way the self-feeding is done is to cut a table or ledge all along one side of the silage heap—from which the cows can pull out the silage as they need it. As the cows clear the table of cut silage we cut down a little further so that they don't have to work too hard to pull it out. In this way they can get as much as they want; and a Jersey will eat 100-120 lb. a day on which, if it is good silage, she will produce up to 5 gallons of milk a day in good weather conditions. Larger breeds have been known to eat as much as 125-130 lb. a day. If it is not possible to allow as much as this, then, instead of opening up a flat ledge or table of silage and cutting it loose at the back of the ledge, a sloping face must be left with none of the silage actually cut loose. In this way the cows have to pull out the silage themselves. The steeper the slope on the face the less they are able to pull out; until, with a sheer vertical face, it is impossible for them to get any at all. (See diagrams.)

During our first year of this system we didn't fence around or across the clamp—and though they occasionally walked up on top of the heap they didn't seem to do much damage. But now we make the heaps long enough to allow the whole herd to feed along one side only, and run the electric

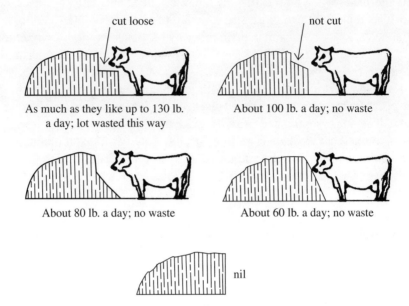

cut loose

not cut

As much as they like up to 130 lb. a day; lot wasted this way

About 100 lb. a day; no waste

About 80 lb. a day; no waste

About 60 lb. a day; no waste

nil

Cross sections of the silage clamp showing how the quantity of silage a cow can take varies with the angle of the feeding face: estimated weights only.

fence over the heap just behind the exposed face. This prevents the cows from getting on top of the heap.

One *disadvantage* is the mud that accumulates around the clamp; but bedding down with clean straw solves this problem, though in exceptionally wet weather frequent bedding with straw is needed. There is also a tendency for boss cows to lie down on this straw with bellies full to chew the cud. Bedding a sheltered area of the field a little distance away from the silage heap will encourage them to leave the table when they have finished eating, and make way for the odd heifer or nervous cow that prefers to eat in solitude.

There is room for experiment in portable 'duckboards' or tracks which can be laid alongside the heap to maintain clean conditions underfoot for the cows feeding at the heap. Wire-netting tracks, however strong or fine-meshed, collect mud and trash and aren't really practicable as it is almost impossible to take them up for use elsewhere. Galvanized iron sheets, with slats rivetted across them, are the best temporary floor for this purpose that

5. Self-service silage 1953, when we used the vertical-ended clamp covered with chalk.

6. The silage heap sometime has to be shovelled out of a snow-drift—but the Jersey yearlings thrive on it.

7. Strip-grazing the late soron rape kale in field adjoining the silage heap.

8. Self-service silage.

I have been able to devise. This can, if necessary, be brushed off each day or week, and full cows do not sit down on them and prevent others from feeding. Fixed on small wheels raising them not more than 9-12 inches from ground level, these 'duckboards' become portable with a tractor.

Where the heap can be permanently sited a concrete base for the heap and the cows is the ideal, with drainage or channels into which the dung can be brushed or bulldozed each day.

You may ask: 'What about indigestion—don't they over eat?' Well, there was a tendency for one or two cows to gorge themselves in the first two days of this unlimited silage feeding, but immediately they realized they could help themselves at any time they became reasonable about it. There was also some bullying. The boss cows kept the heifers away. This merely meant that the heifers had to adjust themselves to a rather later breakfast and they came to the heap when the boss cows went away to lie down and chew the cud.

Costs of growing the silage and the kale are as follows:

Cost of Kale for Strip Grazing

	£	s.	2006* £	$
10 acres cultivation for kale three times rotavated for weed-mulch-fallow	40		947	1,742
Kale seed, 5 lb. an acre at 4s.	10		237	436
Roll-in at 15s. an acre	7	10	178	327
	£57	10	1,361	2,505

or £5 15s. an acre (£140 / $258)

*Editor's note: The author's historic financial data was converted to modern currencies and approximately adjusted for inflation, using the consumer price index. This most certainly will not correlate to modern costs and prices, but should be utilized for general directional trends only.

SELF-SERVICE SILAGE AND KALE

Cost of Silage Making

(Three men and two tractors and buckrakes make
from herbal ley 150 tons weekly.)

	£	2006* £	2006* $
Labour cost	20	488	898
Tractor and fuel	15	366	673
150 tons each year from 12 acres ley costing £16 (£379) an acre (see page 35) lasting 4 years equals an acre each year or approximately 10s a ton.	48	1,171	2,155
	£83	2,025	3,727

Winter Milk Costs per Gallon

	d.	2006* £	2006* $
Silage and Kale	6.8	0.69	1.27
Dredge Corn	3.4	0.35	0.64
Total Food Cost	10.2 d	1.04	1.91
Labour	4.4	0.45	0.83
Herd replacements	*per gallon* 0.22	0.22	0.40
Total cost per gallon	14.82 d	1.51	2.78

Editor's note: The author's historic financial data was converted to modern currencies and approximately adjusted for inflation, using the consumer price index. This most certainly will not correlate to modern costs and prices, but should be utilized for general directional trends only.

This figure covers total outgoings for winter milk production. A complete costing would require the allocation of interest on capital investment, rent, machinery depreciation, etc. But this analysis is a guide for the purposes of comparison with costings carried out by such centres as Bristol University Economics Department and Wye College. I would suggest that any farmer claiming a cheaper or more efficient system of milk production should join with me in having our winter milk production costed by one of these official and impartial bodies. I am prepared to challenge anyone to produce more milk per acre of land used to feed the cattle, at a lower cost per gallon; and this I believe to be the only true measure of efficient milk production.

Labour costs with this system are of course infinitesmal. The silage face needs cutting about two or three times a week, according to the quantity of silage allowed. The electric fence is moved back on the kale each day—a matter of a few minutes.

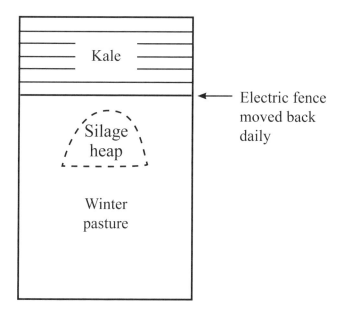

With heifers and dry cows, even less frequent cutting of the face of the heap is needed, as they can be left to work rather harder than the cows, pulling out the silage from a much more sheer face.

With 30 cows in milk, one man does all the work of milking and feeding them and all the followers, and has time left to do a few hours' field work during the day. This means that he milks, turns out the cows, washes the sheds and milking machine, feeds the calves with their hand-feed of silage. There is no bucket-feeding to do as they merely suckle nurse cows which come in and out with the milking herd. On the tractor he visits the heifers and dry stock at their silage heap as he goes out for three or four hours' field work each day.

One good man can quite easily milk 50 cows through a milking parlour, do all the feeding by the self-service silage system, and tend naturally suckled calves, and in addition attend to a thousand or two hopper-fed deep-litter hens, filling the hoppers twice a week and collecting the eggs each day.

CHAPTER IV

The Cow for the Job

Perhaps the most important essential for this system is the right cow for the job.

Obviously cows which may have been bred in test tubes, reared on calf gruel, milked on high protein concentrates, kept alive on synthetic minerals and trace elements, and frequently subjected to sulphonamides and penicillin and the germ-free D.D.T.-laden air of the modern milking parlour, will not take readily to a diet of roughage and fresh air.

Similarly the flat-sided, short-legged show-ring specimen with all bag and no body, will not wear well through a winter of walking to the silage heap, ripping out her own rations and spreading her own dung. What is more, on the heavy land, with her feet and udder daily dragging through mud, she is constantly liable to succumb to foot and udder troubles. Then there is the terrifying task of keeping the udders clean enough to maintain TT standards of milk production.

When we first started our self-service system and wintering our cattle out, my herdsman and I both had many a nightmare dreaming of the mud-covered udders of our best type low-chassised show cows, which took us longer to clean than to milk each morning. We are now experimenting with washable plastic brassieres for the cows which can be washed down with a hose when the cows come in to be milked, then slipped off for milking and replaced when the cows go out to the silage clamp again.

But it also became evident to us that we must breed a different type of cow. Two inches extra length in the leg made all the difference between clean teats and teats from which it was impossible to remove all the caked mud, to say nothing of the bruised and cracked skin which resulted from over-much scrubbing and scraping. Similarly an extra inch or two of width between the hind legs gave the necessary clearance between lifted feet (as the cow walked) and the sides of the udder. Cow or sickle hocks are of course impossible for this system, for they have the inevitable effect of levering the feet up to the udder and stomach at every step, plastering both with mud.

We had already bred the big-bellied cow by years of selection and natural feeding; but apart from the important essential of strong, straight legs, which served us well in this system, we had made the orthodox error of believing there was some virtue in short legs. This is really an attribute of good beef-cattle and how it came to be accepted by dairy-cattle breeders I really cannot imagine. Short legs would be all right on shallow bodies, and I am certainly aware that many high concentrate feeders have bred shallow bodies. But we don't want eithershallow bodies or flat sides. Deep and wide barrels are absolutely essential to enable the cow to consume and digest large quantities of bulky food. Fortunately, in my herd we have got the barrels to deal with this bulk feeding. Now we must fit these bulk-food barrels with longer legs and broader backsides and we shall have the perfect cow for the job.

Whether such cows will ever satisfy the show judges is another matter. But they will certainly satisfy the inevitable trend of modern farming practice towards low-cost livestock husbandry with a high output per man employed.

A longer-legged cow may not be so pleasing to the eye, but there is no real indication that the length of leg has any bearing on milk output. My herd has shown that, provided body and bag are in robust conformity to the needs of heavy bulk feeding and heavy milk production, the only essential requirements for the legs are straightness and strength. The indications are that the longer-legged cows are, if anything, the more efficient converters of food into milk. But whether length of leg has the remotest influence on the animals' efficiency in converting food into milk I would not argue at this stage in my observations, for I would hesitate to be dogmatic on such inconclusive evidence. The relationship of longer leg to food-conversion efficiency is probably due to the longer-legged cow being a rather slimmer type, generally carrying less flesh, with less inclination to convert food to body fat than the shorter-legged cow, which is traditionally a beefier type, more inclined to convert its food into body fat than into milk.

What is important in this consideration of the changes in cow types that are necessary for the efficient operation of my natural-feeding system, is that we need not fear that longer legs are so undesirable as the show judge has persuaded us in the past. And the inevitable acceptance of this winter-milk-at-summer-cost-system, will make the leggier cow more popular, at least among men who have to wash the udders!

CHAPTER V

Self-feeding for the Soil

Self-feeding, Self-fertilizing, Self-restoring Rotation

Fertility farming—building the fertility of the soil simultaneously with cropping it—has not been popular, especially in official circles, because, since 1939 maximum production at any price has been official policy. It has mattered little that maximum production of chemically-boosted crops has resulted in diminishing fertility for both the soil and the animal, and an increase in degenerative diseases for the ultimate human consumer. The farmer who has dared to put his future soil-fertility on an equal level of importance with productivity has been in perpetual danger of supervision or dispossession by the Agricultural Committees.

Now *real* efficiency is at last officially permitted. Production is at last beginning, in official circles, to be related to the cost of achieving it; and soil fertility can now once more become a paramount consideration of good farming.

In this chapter I have described the rotation which lends itself admirably to my system of dependence on silage supported by kale in the winter, and entirely on the herbal ley in the summer. This also enables one to gain maximum soil-fertility at minimum cost by using the cows as dung-spreaders as well as silage-carters and converters.

I am using this rotation in reclaiming old worn-out pastures on my present farm.

In the first year, one end of the field is ploughed or rotavated in the spring or early summer, and worked periodically to get it clean and start the decomposition of the old turf.

In June or early July, into the broken section of the pasture, Thousand-headed kale is sown with a corn drill in rows seven inches apart. The roller follows the drill and no further treatment is given to the kale. It thrives on

9. The short legs of an orthodox show winner—are not ideal for keeping the udder out of the mud.

10. The longer legs of Polden Chocolate Cake keep the udder clean. It may be suggested that the long-legged cow is not the best milker. Polden Chocolate Cake gave 8,800 lb. 5.73% B.F. 1st calf—almost the same as shortlegged Polden Haughty Hetty with her 1st calf (see plates 22 & 23).

11. A silage heap in the distance and young hungry gap kale in the foreground.

12. A close-up of the same heap as plate 11.

the decaying turf and produces a leafy plant of kale which is easily grazed behind an electric fence.

The silage heap is made just over on the unploughed portion of the pasture so that the cows may help themselves to silage and kale behind the electric fence—lying back on to the old pasture.

Kale sown on upchurned old turf is ideal for strip-grazing because the turf prevents the soil from becoming too muddy in the winter.

In the second spring, the kale ground is disced or rotavated and sown with oats and vetches, undersown with a herbal ley mixture or sown direct with the ley after cutting the oats and vetches for silage. Another piece of the pasture is broken up and sown to Thousand-headed kale.

The silage heap moves down the field, once more adjoining the kale section.

In the autumn a second silage heap is made from the oats and vetches sown on the first section of the field, leaving the ley underneath for grazing and/or silage in the following spring.

In the third spring we have the herbal ley on the first section, which may be grazed early and then mown to make a silage heap on the old section of the field. The second section which was kale is disced and sown to oats and vetches, and a fourth section is broken for kale. The silage heap is moved down once more on to the old unbroken pasture.

In the fourth spring the second section adds to the area of ley available for grazing and silage. The third section, kale stubble, is disced or rotavated and sown to oats and vetches, undersown or aftersown with a ley, and the fourth section is broken for kale.

This process is continued until the whole field has been broken and sown down to a good herbal ley. In the last year the silage heap will have to be made on one of the new ley sections and the oats and vetches section, which is then the last but one section in the field, is sown immediately after the oats and vetches are cut and gathered for silage, to a winter rye or other winter green grazing crop, undersown with ley if early enough in the autumn (i.e. early September), or to be sown down direct with the last piece from which the kale has been grazed, in the spring.

The immense amount of fertility built into the soil by this system comes in a number of ways.

Firstly, everything grown in the field is fed on the field, so that the field grows its own sustenance, passed through the cows, and dunged back rich in nitrogen, potash, and phosphates, and the trace elements derived from the subsoil of adjoining fields brought up by the herbal ley from which the silage was made. When the new ley sections of the field are also going into the silage on the field itself—then the field begins to regenerate its own fertility from its own subsoil (i.e. minerals and trace elements brought up by the deep-rooting herbs of the ley).

If possible each section of the field should be subsoiled either before the kale is sown or before the oats and vetches are sown. In this way the subsoil is opened up ready for the herbal ley which follows the oats and vetches.

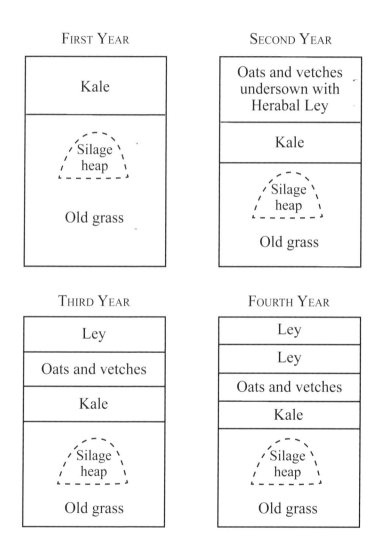

FIRST YEAR

Kale

Silage heap

Old grass

SECOND YEAR

Oats and vetches undersown with Herabal Ley

Kale

Silage heap

Old grass

THIRD YEAR

Ley

Oats and vetches

Kale

Silage heap

Old grass

FOURTH YEAR

Ley

Ley

Oats and vetches

Kale

Silage heap

Old grass

Secondly, there are few crops better than oats and vetches for putting nitrogen into the soil. And this is free nitrogen gathered from the atmosphere by the nitrifying bacteria of the vetches—organic nitrogen—the kind which is best for the young ley which is to follow.

You will have no difficulties in establishing a ley from old pasture where a kale crop and an oat and vetch crop have intervened. The decaying turf has released, by means of the organic acids of decay bringing them into solution, the unavailable minerals which are present in every soil if only they can be released. As I have said elsewhere, given a few leaves of organic matter for anchorage, sustenance, and the dissolution of a minute portion of the rock, nature can grow a vigorous and healthy plant actually on a rock. The criterion of crop growing in any part of the world is nothing more complex than the presence of a little moisture-holding, nutrient-releasing organic matter. In other words the secret of establishing a ley is biological and not chemical. I have explained in more detail in another chapter *(Making a Ley with a Mower)* how a perfect ley can be established on a mineral- and lime-deficient soil without the use of any synthetic sustenance.

This, then, is the third free source of fertility inherent in this system.

Fourthly, the strip-grazing of the kale concentrates an even surface dressing of dung on to the kale section each year, applied far more thoroughly and evenly than by hand or machine, and effectively incorporated into the top soil by the trampling feet of the cattle themselves. A valuable interval of time intervenes for the action of rain, atmosphere and soil organisms to commence their processing of the dung before it is churned into a rich seed-bed by the disc harrow or rotary hoe.

Fifthly, and perhaps the real centre-piece in this jig-saw pattern of fertility, is the self-service silage heap, radiating from all angles of the heap the rich manurial value which the cow is continually depositing as she feeds at the heap, and moves to and from the heap in her journeys to the grass to lie and cud, or to the kale to stand and graze. As the silage heap moves across the field each year this concentration of fertility gradually covers the whole field. But as the greatest fertility is always at the site of the heap, additional value may be obtained by shifting the heap from side to side of the field according to where the less fertile areas of the field may be.

Two additions to this self-feeding, self-fertilizing programme—one for the heifers and dry stock and one for the milking herd— are the incorporation into the system of the self-feeding of straw and hay.

A system I first saw deliberately practised in Eire in 1946 is the building of a hay or straw stack in a field in which cattle are to be wintered, and allowing the cattle to pull out the hay or straw as they need it. By this method they gather from the hay or straw both food and shelter. The small residue, trampled under and dunged upon, is forked up into a compost heap when the cattle have finished.

With cattle that are not in milk, where unlimited straw may be allowed, the combination of this straw-feeding system with the self-fed silage and kale provides a way of using straw and increasing the amount of manure available to spread on the field. One snag, however, is that very little of the straw is eaten whenever there is good silage available, and this even applies to hay. It seems that even the best hay is less palatable than good silage and kale.

WEATHERPROOF HAYMAKING

But hay made on tripods *is* attractive, and is the only hay in my experience which offers any comparison with good silage. If you still hang on to the tradition of hay being an essential part of winter feeding (my cows have had no hay, except for limited experiments, for six years) here is a new way of using it.

An adaptation, combining the tripod principle with the Swedish or Norwegian fence or rack system, makes it possible to allow self-feeding of hay in the field in which it was made. This can be yet another variation of the triple self-feeding field described earlier, making it a fourfold feeding system, i.e. self-feeding of the soil, self-feeding silage, self-feeding kale, and self-feeding hay.

The hay is made from grass cut on the lie-back section of the field (the portion not yet broken) or, as some of the earlier sections of the field are re-established as new leys—from them.

The grass is cut and tedded as for tripod haymaking, and, after a few hours' wilting, swept to either hedge with buckrakes which deposit the hay on a several-stranded wire fence, with the fence set at the same angle as the buckrake to allow the buck-rake to drop the hay on the wire rack or fence.

Further supplies of hay are forked on top of the fence by hand to give a sloping rainproof roof to the hay heaped up on the fence. The free-circulation of air under and around the fence quickly dries the hay, which may be lightly thatched or covered with a plastic or sisalcraft material until ready for use. An electric fence keeps the cows away from the hay until they are allowed free access to help themselves to the fence along the headland of the field.

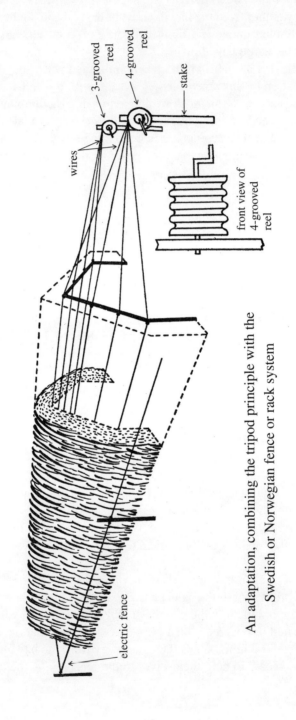

An adaptation, combining the tripod principle with the
Swedish or Norwegian fence or rack system

The fence system of haymaking and feeding is of course developed from my experience of the wonderful hay which is to be had by the use of the tripod system. Where the hay is not to be self-fed and can be stacked or baled from actual tripods, the following system is the one I have used for the past ten years.

This tripod system means I can plan to make my hay, as soon as the crop is ready, without having to watch my grass growing coarse and losing its feeding value—waiting week after week for the weather to be fine. Before I started weatherproof haymaking ten years ago, as each June came round my life became a perpetual worry about the weather, and my hair began to grow rapidly greyer every year. Now I can make the hay when the grass is at its best; and what is more, it is hay with a 20 per cent protein content, as green as the best dried grass and with a higher food value. Each year now, instead of greyer *hair* I have greener hay!

We started with straight 7-8 ft. larch- or Douglas-fir poles, making the tripods ourselves, linking them at one end with wire so that they fold together when not in use. When erected upright, we fixed similar, but lighter, horizontal poles, resting about a foot from the ground across the base of each tripod leg. A triangle of wire goes around half-way up to keep the hay out of the centre. This forms the shell of the tripod hut upon which we build the hay. We found, however, that it was much cheaper to buy the ready-made tripods and get the expert instruction of the patentees of the original system. With experienced tripod haymaking it is easy to produce a higher-protein fodder than with any other system, including grass drying; but if the tripods are built badly, it is easier still to produce fodder no better than farmyard manure and even less palatable!

When we start tripod haymaking, each day we cut with the mower as much grass as we can put on tripods the next day; the quantity depends on the number of men available. Two experienced men can build a tripod hut, holding about 5 cwt. of hay, in about twenty minutes. This means that four men, with the aid of a sweep or a buckrake to bring the hay to the tripod, can build at the rate of about 30 cwt. an hour. Allowing for stoppages, four men building tripods, with another man sweeping in the hay, will make a two-ton-an-acre crop at the rate of about five acres a day.

It is important to follow the mower immediately with the type of *kick* tedder which throws the grass into the air and lets it fall lightly to the ground to wilt. With a crop of about 30 cwt. an acre, what is cut in the morning, provided it is immediately loaded and the weather is good, can be put on to the tripods in the afternoon or evening. But a two-ton an acre, or heavier crop, is best left until the following day before being put on the tripods. Deciding when it is ready to go on the tripods does not require as much experience or skill as deciding when hay, under orthodox systems, is ready to bale or to stack. If it has no *external* moisture, green wilted grass may usually be put on the tripods within 18-24 hours after cutting, with no risk of damage at all if it is not too tightly built. An experienced tripodder will start to build his tripods much sooner than that.

The aim in building the hut is to get a conical funnel internally, with a thin shell of hay as vertical as possible on the outside. The first 'shelf' or foundation of grass is laid on the horizontal poles or triangular wire which form a ledge a foot or so from the base of the tripod. The wall of hay is built up on that, placing the grass on as lightly and loosely as possible. Start by hand, and then throw each small forkful gently on to the shelf, moving round and round as the hut grows. If you have been used to building stacks you'll find it hard to avoid the temptation to pat it down. But you must allow as much air as possible to get in; build so lightly that the hay virtually sits on air. The centre of the tripod must be kept hollow throughout the building operation until the hay has reached about one foot above the apex of the tripod; then, a large round forkful is dropped on, to round off and 'waterproof the top. Tie it down with twine, tying it over the top from the base of one leg to the base of another, if it is likely to be windy.

Once on the tripods the hay is safe for as long as it needs to be left there. It can be self-fed from the tripods by use of the electric fence—rationing out the tripods daily, and running a strand from the main fence around each tripod, to prevent the huts being knocked down as the hay is pulled off by the cows.

Alternatively, sweep or buckrake the tripod hut complete to the baler or stack elevator, or move from hut to hut with a pick-up baler.

The finer points of weatherproof haymaking must be learned from the tripod manufacturers themselves, or from one of the increasing number of farmers who have said good-bye to haymaking worries and invested in this weatherproof system. If you have never tried tripod haymaking yourself, I *do* urge you to go and see some this year and bring some of the green, high-protein hay back with you for your cows to try. I am sure you will never make hay the worrying way again.

13. Pulling out the silage from the almost sheer face of the heap.

14. Well in to the vertical end of our 1953 self-service silage.

Tripod Haymaking

15. (1) Sweeping from the swathe to the tripod with a buckrake; (2) The tripod with air vent trestles ready to receive the grass; (3) Building commences; (4) The bottom shelf of hay laid on the wire or crosspiece poles; (5) Built up to the 'shoulder' of the trestles; (6) Ready for the cap. Note the ideal shape for a completed tripod hut in the background of each picture: vertical sides and tall, rather than squat.

CHAPTER VI

Natural Crop Nutrition

When I was farming in Ireland I always noticed that the cottager's goat and donkey had abundant grazing long before there was any hope of pasture, even on the most forward leys, on my farm. The Irishman's 'long acre'—the banks and hedgerows of the roadside—upon which the landless maintained considerable numbers of grazing animals—provided lush growth a month or more before cattle could be turned on to even the best managed farm pastures.

This happens everywhere in the world, but it struck me more forcibly in Ireland because the 'long acre'—as the Irish call the free pasturing of the roadsides—is made much more use of in Ireland; and I became as green as the banks with envy, when my well-treated fields grew hardly a blade of grass, while a cottager with barely a back garden was feeding his goats, donkey, turkeys and maybe even a couple of cows, for nothing.

Why is the hedgerow growth so much earlier and quicker to recover after grazing than the field growth? Can we imitate the conditions of the hedgerow to reproduce the same early and abundant growth in the field?

It is not difficult to discover the reasons for this superiority of nature in the hedgerows and to apply them in establishing our cultivated pastures. The herbal ley comes as near as possible to this ideal pasture, so long as the soil conditions of the hedgerow, as well as the variety and type of ingredients, are imitated for the ley.

What, then, has the hedgerow grazing got that the field has not?

I summarize these desirable factors as follows:

(1) Ideal soil conditions—i.e. fertility, friability, moisture-holding capacity, and warmth from bacterially-generated heat.

(2) Shelter—the hedge acting as a cloche to encourage an early start to all crops growing under or near it.

(3) Deep-rooted ingredients and early-starting herbs.

Each autumn nature begins to prepare the soil for the early spring growth of the following year. Seeds of all varieties fall into an already warm, moist and friable soil. Then starts a succession of leaf-falls of various kinds, which, intermixed with a tiny proportion of animal wastes, covers the seeds. A slow process of decay, through which the fallen leaves then begin to pass, assisted by rain-given moisture held in the surface sponge of organic material, creates all the warmth and nutriment that the seed needs to germinate and grow. The seed which contains the nucleus of life is covered, warmed and fed by leaves which have died and fallen from the trees, bushes and grasses above the soil. During their growing period those leaves have gathered the raw materials of chlorophyll, vitamins, minerals, trace elements, proteins and sugars from soil, sun and air, and in addition, no doubt, many elements of which we know nothing, from sources of which we are even yet not aware. These are transferred by the leaves to the surface soil to join in the work of soil bacteria, mycelia, fungi and the minute living creatures of the soil, to supply, in adequate quantities and ideal proportions, every single requirement of health, nutrition and growth for the young plant as well as for the established bush and tree.

No synthetic nutrient need be added and, because the resultant crop is always naturally healthy, no poison sprays are needed to 'protect' the plants from pests and diseases.

In spite of the complete absence of artificial nutrients or stimulants, the roadside grasses, clovers and herbs, quickly recover and produce fresh growth after frequent cuttings by council roadmen in Britain and the grazing of 'long-acre' livestock in Ireland. How much more ought we to harvest from our pastures, even *without* chemical stimulants, were we able to imitate these ideal soil conditions of the hedge bottom. For we have the advantage of generations of selective breeding of leafy strains of grasses and clovers, in addition to the natural herbage of the hedgerow, from which to constitute our leys.

But the fact is, that on most farms, little or no attempt is made even to observe, let alone profit by nature's methods of soil preparation and fertility building. When I first observed how nature got at least one month ahead of me in providing 'early bite', I too was following the accepted system of soil cultivation, with all its attendant costs in fertilizers and health supplements (which were made necessary by the inadequate diet which resulted). But once having recognized the superior method of soil management and manuring, I quickly started to adapt my ley preparation to it.

I needed no scientific confirmation of a method I had observed with my own eyes to be superior and less costly than any accepted method of achieving ideal soil conditions for early growth. The simple comparison of growth in the field and around the hedgerows, provided convincing evidence from the only really genuine scientist—nature. Facts are good enough for most farmers without the supporting explanations of laboratory-bound professors, though men who have gone to the fields for practical information have since supported nature's methods of cultivation and manuring as the best means of ensuring constant foolproof fertility, instead of the misleading and variable measure of chemical analysis.

Over twenty years ago Sir Albert Howard insisted on the importance of the biological, as distinct from the chemical, assessment of soil fertility. He declared that chemical soil analysis was, at very best, nothing more than a rough guide, to be checked against physical examination and a close observation of biological and botanical indications.

When he first visited me at Goosegreen, we discussed this subject at length. He had made suggestions which were contrary to the indications of a recent soil analysis. 'Forget the soil test,' he said, 'look at the weeds that are growing there.'

I had grown up under old-fashioned farming conditions, and a father who was suspicious of the mathematical tyranny of soil-analyses and other scientific arrogance. The true farmer knew his soil by its feel in his hand and under his feet, and by the plants which nourished under natural conditions. We knew that the heaviest crops resulted from the most muck, whatever N, P, or K a soil analysis might suggest. So what Sir Albert said made sense to me.

When, with the change-over to surface cultivation, I found that keeping organic matter in the top few inches of soil resulted in increased crops and the apparent correction of 'soil deficiencies,' I described the phenomenon in my book *Fertility Farming*. Dr. Dahr, head of the chemistry department of Alahabad University, visited me and said that what I was doing on a farm scale to demonstrate the biological release of plant nutrients, confirmed experiments in which he had shown that the chemical analysis of the soil was profoundly influenced by the method of application of organic matter; that surface application, in the presence of sunlight, added not only the chemical constituents of the organic matter itself, but collected and manufactured, by photosynthesis and bacterial action, additional quantities of essential elements and released further otherwise unavailable minerals in the top soil, during the process of decomposition. Soil analyses were thus useless, as they would vary according to biological activity, which in turn varied with seasonal sunlight, rain, and surface organic deposits of crop residues and insect and bacterial life.

Sir Albert's view of soil analyses was thus justified; my own experiments and claims recounted in *Fertility Farming* were scientifically confirmed; and our assertions regarding the complete adequacy of organic methods, and in particular organic surface cultivation, were firmly established.

As though to clinch the matter, we were further supported by Struthers and Sieling of Massachusetts University, who declared that organic matter on the surface of the soil has the ability to collect from the atmosphere 'aerosols' containing phosphates and calcium, and that adequate surface organic matter was the best means of maintaining and increasing essential available nutrients in the top soil.

Additional scientific evidence in support of Sir Albert's inspired judgment and my own practical claims has also now been published by the Soil Association.

I am grateful to Lady Eve Balfour, who inspired the Haughley Project, where this recent work has been done, for the following summary of a report which serious students of soil fertility should get from the Soil Association and read in full. The Haughley experiment is divided into three sections: (1) Organic only, (2) Mixed-organic and chemical, (3) Stockless. Monthly soil analyses on each of the three sections confirms the following:

(1) The fallacy of a single soil analysis to determine soil requirements.

(2) The relationship between high organic content and mineral availability.

(3) The effect that different crops appear to have on mineral availability.

(4) The fact that minerals recovered in crops bear little relation to fertilizer applications.

Numbers 1, 2 and 3 have been revealed by the soil analyses which were carried out every month on every field for the following: pH, Total Nitrogen, Available Phosphorus, Available Potassium, Humus, Water-holding Capacity. Some variations in pH occurred, but in the main the figure is fairly constant at around eight on all three sections. Sectional averages for total Nitrogen are: Stockless 15 percent, Mixed 20 percent, Organic 25 percent. For Humus (determined by loss on ignition) comparative figures average approximately: Stockless 6 percent, Mixed 7 percent, Organic 8 percent. In the case of available potash and phosphate, however, very striking seasonal variations were recorded. These variations occurred on all sections, but markedly less on the Stockless section. So far as it is at present possible to relate this release of plant nutrients to other factors, observations have shown that:

(a) all fields are low in available phosphate and potash during the winter;

(b) there is a tendency for the figures to rise steadily, as the season advances, to a peak in June or July, subsequently falling;

(c) the peak is highest in those fields which have a high organic matter and total nitrogen content;

(d) it is greatest under arable crops, which make a quick demand, and least under leys, which have steady growth and at the same time are continually grazed off;

(e) it is greatest of all under barley;

(f) it bears little if any relation to fertilizer application, except that the smallest release of these important plant nutrients occurs on those fields which have regular fertilizer treatment and no livestock.

The most dramatic variation occurred in the case of an old permanent pasture which was ploughed for the first time five years previous to the tests. Since then it grew four consecutive arable crops and, except for a light dressing of compost to one acre, received no manure or fertilizer treatment of any kind. In this field the analysis in June showed nearly ten times more available phosphate and potash than was present in January. The crop in this field was barley, and the actual figures compared with fields growing barley in the other two sections were:

ORGANIC

	Av. Phosphate	Av. Potash	Total N.
January	10	6	500
June	81	44	580
July	38	26	500
November	27	8	450

MIXED

	Av. Phosphate	Av. Potash	Total N.
January	6	6	210
June	50	20	330
July	42	28	400
November	20	11	240

STOCKLESS

	Av. Phosphate	Av. Potash	Total N.
January	11	4	150
June	26	10	200
July	26	14	240
November	13	9	170

The peak figures occur sometimes in June and sometimes in July, thus ruling out weather as the only determining factor. Both the Mixed and Stockless fields received approximately the same quantities of NPK fertilizers, applied to the Mixed at the end of February, and to the Stockless at the end of March. Thus the rise in these two cases, though possibly affected by the fertilizer, bears little quantitative relation to it. There does, however, appear to be a connection between the release of the mineral and the total nitrogen content. Summarizing this part of the work, Dr. R. F. Milton, who conducted the experiment, says: 'Surprising variations were established throughout the year. These were most marked on the Organic section where no artificials were used—the highest rise in available minerals and nitrogen occurred in those fields with the highest humus content.

'This rise was due to the release of bound minerals by the action of soil bacteria and/or fungi and the soil bacteria are most active where the content of organic matter is high.'

The fact that minerals recovered in a crop bear little relation to fertilizer application can best be illustrated by comparing the figures for three fields under the same crop in the same section. The following table shows the amounts in cwts. per acre of P_2O_5 (phosphoric acid), K (potassium) and N (nitrogen) in the three barley crops on the Stockless section, side by side with the amounts (also in cwt. per acre) applied as fertilizer to the fields.

It is interesting to compare the above with the two fields of Organic barley which received no treatment,

Field	Bulk Yield Cwt.	Mineral Yield in Crop per acre in cwt.			Mineral Application, cwt. p.a.		
		K	P_2O_5	N	K	P_2O_5	N
S: No. 1	10	.04	.07	.13	.24	.43	.22
S: No. 2	19	.07	.11	.18	.19	.34	.40
S: No. 3	18½	.08	.11	.28	.20	.36	.18

The equivalent figures for the Mixed section field of barley were as follows:

| M. | 15 ½ | .06 | .10 | .24 | 2.29 | 1.03 | 1.79 |

(Application figures here include F Y M.)

It is interesting to compare the above with the two fields of Organic barley which received no treatment,

O: No. 1	22	.09	.12	.23	Nil
O: No. 2	18	.07	.12	.33	Nil

The most striking comparison to be noted in the figures, these particularly in regard to nitrogen, is between fields No. 2 and No. 3 on the Stockless section and No. 2 on the Organic section, since there was little difference in bulk yield between these three fields.

The practical results obtained on mine, and a number of other organic farms, by the mere maintenance of organic matter, without chemicals, supported by the scientific experiments of Dr. Dahr and the Soil Association, make it clear that soil analyses are useless as a guide to crop needs, or as a measure of soil fertility.

Ample organic matter either supplies or releases all that is needed for soil and crop nutrition.

Sir John Russell in *Soil Conditions and Plant Growth* quotes a number of scientific authorities in support of the organic system of soil and crop nutrition. He even states that nature somehow manages without chemical additions, due to this complete nutritional process which we have observed in places where natural growth is earliest and best:

'While plants *can* grow satisfactorily and attain full development with inorganic nutrients only, yet, in natural conditions their nutrition *always* proceeds in presence of organic matter . . . (My italics.—F. N. T.)

'In the Rothamsted field experiments with cereals, no combination of artificial fertilizers is as effective as farmyard manure in avoiding deterioration of yield on continuously cropped land, or in steadying crop yields from year to year, but the effects could be attributed to differences in nutrient supply or to physical and physico-chemical actions of the manure on the soil . . .'

Russell says "The Rothamsted mangold plots receiving no organic manure, 'get into so sticky and "unkindly" a state that the young plants have some difficulty in surviving, however much food is supplied, and may fail altogether in a dry spring; the dunged plots rich in humus are much more favourable to the plant *and never fail to give a crop."* (My emphasis.— F. N. T.)

So marked are the physical effects of organic matter, he continues, 'that if 15 or 20 percent, of organic matter is present in a soil the operation of other factors ceases to count for much, and the distinction between sands, loams, and clays tend to be obliterated.'

In other words: if we could imitate the soil conditions of the hedgerow closely enough, we could forget the perennial problems of the intractable clay or the blow-away sand. We should have only fertile soil as distinct from our accepted variations of clay soil, sandy soil, red marl or loam. Because the achievement of a universal fertile soil is difficult, that is no argument against striving to get as near to it as practical circumstances allow.

K. T. Hartley and M. Greenwood, writing in the *Empire Journal of Experimental Agriculture* in 1933, at the time I was an agricultural student at Leeds University, reported that in Nigeria 'small applications of farmyard manure at the rate of only one ton an acre had effects considerably surpassing an equivalent mixture of artificial manures.'

In 1872 Grandeau claimed that organic matter played the chief part in the nitrogen and phosphorous nutrition of plants. This has of course since been explained by the ability of decaying organic matter to release acids which render the insoluble phosphates freely soluble, and by the nitrifying action of bacteria which depend upon organic matter for their existence.

As a working farmer, I take the view (apart altogether from any other considerations) that if my land will produce good crops, which *I know* are of better quality, without any chemicals, I am better off without buying any. With fields of my size, if a test were taken in January, I should have to spend perhaps another £100 more, if I believed the salesman, than if he had done his analysis in June or July when the phosphates and potash were up. It is much cheaper for me to wait till I have farmed the minerals into an available condition in my soil, than to buy them in synthetic form because the genuine organic potash and phosphates happen to be 'out' the day the analyst calls!

Rothamsted figures show that the top eight inches of my soil have more than enough minerals to crop it for a century, and my deep-rooting herbs run lower than that, some down to ten feet and more. Some people who go by theory will then say that I, and the many others like me, are robbing the soil. If Dr. Struther and Professor Selling are wrong about aerosols, which I take to be mineral dust blowing through the air, then maybe in about a thousand years I shall have made a desert!

To save the man who will be as far from me in time as the Saxons were before William the Conqueror came down my way, they consider I ought to add relatively trifling quantities (compared with what is already there) of chemicals, manufactured from synthetic acids and rock-deposit raw material which is going to be exhausted as quickly as coal. But I rather think that the man who has my farm in the year 2,054 is going to be pretty mean with the superphosphate and potash. For fertilizer prices are going to be wicked by then as they get scarcer, manufacturing costs increase and shareholders' dividends have to be maintained.

Taking a long view, longer than that expected of any other industry (for no one expects an oil company to think of the future with hard cash paid out now), there is a consolation:

All the deserts of the world have got the criminal who made them in plain view; shortage of water, resulting from the removal of trees, or letting the rain wash the nutriment out of the soil, by shifting cultivation as in Africa, or breaking up good pasture and robbing it by mono-cropping, as in America.

There is a good deal of first-class grass in the world—or there was until men started looting it for quick gain. Nature never farms the land into a desert by taking cash crops of oak trees, as an example, for a thousand years from one forest. Consider the American prairie, or the South African veldt, which is a balanced herbal ley that suits the climate. Either carried pretty heavy stocks of game, grazing on the rotational system as they moved about, just as I do with my cattle. This kind of land builds up a great store of fertility, until science moves in and tries to mass-produce groundnuts, or introduces some other way of short-circuiting nature to get rich quick.

This is of course a purely theoretical argument. For our whole idea of what plant foods there are in the land depends so far on soil analysis; and as we have seen how that varies so widely with the seasons, it is more like an elastic tape-measure than a scientific certainty. So, I go only by results; and if I can get my results without fertilizers, I shall keep my money in my pocket, and do my duty by my land as men have done through all the centuries of farming before chemicals were invented.

* * *

In getting the ideal soil conditions for the ley, and preparing a seed-bed of hedgerow quality and fertility, there are two things I have to achieve.

(a) A moisture-holding skin of organic matter on the surface of the soil. I have to give my soil a sponge-cake covering instead of a hard pie-crust! The sponge-cake absorbs and holds moisture, the pie-crust throws it off.

(b) Having achieved a friable humus-rich soil I must apply in the late summer or autumn of the seeding year a surface mulch of vegetation in imitation of the leaf fall.

If these two essentials are achieved I find that soil analyses can be utterly ignored. Conditions for perfect establishment of the ley are automatically created.

CHAPTER VII

Using Weeds to Build Fertility

That most weeds produce a far greater abundance of seeds than our domestic crops is a characteristic the significance of which seems to have escaped the orthodox botanist. Or, if the botanist has followed up the clue to its logical explanation, the resultant revelations have not been acted upon by the agriculturist. For clearly no plant is so profuse in its seeding or persistent in its growth unless it has an essential and very important part in the pattern of nature. If practically all the plants which seed themselves by the million and are apparently impossible to eradicate without poison sprays, are, in the eyes of man 'weeds', that is surely the fault of man, who has failed to discover the useful purpose with which I am convinced each weed has been endowed.

Man's task is not to destroy out of hand everything in nature which he has so far failed to employ for his own immediate profit. Man has no reasonable grounds for assuming that because a plant appears to be an obstacle to his immediate purpose, it is necessarily a thing to be despised and destroyed. It is more than likely that man's immediate purpose is misguided, not that the plant is misplaced.

It is surely unintelligent in the extreme to kill or destroy any animal or plant whose service in the universe we have failed to appreciate. We should rather apply such intelligence as we have in seeking the place and purpose of each living thing in the design of nature. I have found this one of the most satisfying exercises of the human mind, heart and hands. And I am unashamed in advocating the use of the heart in such human endeavour. Far too many of man's pursuits are restricted to brain and brawn; and when any emotion is allowed to creep in, it is only at the lowest level, stimulating the lowest instincts, with no reference to the finest attributes usually associated with the influence of the heart.

In the study of plants as in the study of animals I have tried to make such principles operate; and the result has been a considerable simplification of some hitherto unfathomable farm problems. And in this context comes my discovery of the value of farm weeds, and the development of a system of utilizing, in ways which prevent them from becoming a nuisance, plants which before were an unmitigated pest in my cropping rotation.

The best way to deal with a nuisance is to turn it to good use, especially if it is not easy or economical to get rid of it. As a student of herbs for animal health and soil fertility, I am sure this is the right approach to weeds. Consequently, forsome years I have used much of my land and time in experiments on the utilization and control of the common weeds of the farm.

Such experiments meant first encouraging the weeds to grow in sufficient numbers to different stages of maturity, then using them, and later controlling them in various ways. In spite of some rude comments from my neighbours, I have been able to learn that practically every weed which we regard as a pest, can be managed in such a way as to make use of it at certain stages of the rotation and to eliminate it at others.

COUCH is about the only exception. For, though it has valuable medicinal properties, being a tonic to kidneys, bladder and reproductive system, with anti-sterility powers, it doesn't readily share a field with other crops. It prefers a virtual monopoly of the soil, and therefore if ever it is to be used it will probably only be as a separate permanent crop and not in conjunction with other domestic crops; and that may quite well be a possibility, for I believe the most persistent things in nature are persistent for a good purpose if only we can find it. But our task at present is to be rid of it, and the only really effective way to do that is to have a summer fallow—a practice which lost favour during and since the war. But if couch has no other purpose than to make us take a summer fallow now and then, it has a value. I still believe the biblical sabbath year is an essential of good husbandry.

CREEPING THISTLES, the next most troublesome weed, can be used and at the same time eliminated in a silage crop. A lucerne mixture is the best for this purpose. Thistles are a good source of protein and also have a beneficial effect on the breeding capacity of animals. A district officer of the Agricultural Committee told me that the highest protein silage he had seen was made from a mixture predominantly of thistles. A lucerne mixture sown on a thistly field will eliminate the thistles in three years of cutting for silage two or three times a year. But the thistles should be allowed to grow nearly to maturity each time before they're cut, for the destruction to be complete. Thistles in grassland can also be cleared by allowing them fully to grow and mowing in July. Most of us *encourage* our grassland thistles by cutting them too soon and so encouraging the root development.

NETTLES are one of the richest known sources of protein in nature, and for this reason of all weeds the nettle offers probably the best possibilities for development as a commercial crop. Comfrey, the *greatest* yielder of protein, is already accepted as a farm crop, thanks to the recent researches of Mr. Lawrence D. Hills and the Henry Doubleday Research Association. Nettle hay is well known as a food for goats, and I have made excellent silage for cows from a mixture of nettles and comfrey. As with thistles, nettles may also be destroyed when and where necessary by repeated cutting at maturity—not during the earlier growing stages which, as with thistles, strengthens the root system.

COMFREY is a subject in itself. It is now being used increasingly for pig and poultry feeding and as silage for cattle, being perhaps the heaviest yielding 'weed' in existence when properly cultivated. My present farm is infested with the Russian variety which was used extensively here, during the 1890's, to feed a large stud of horses. I am developing it now for cattle silage and compost material.

DOCKS are valuable as deep-rooting suppliers of minerals and trace elements, but in *very* limited numbers: for docks so quickly get out of hand. Again, they can be eliminated by cutting at maturity—just before they go to seed. And, believe it or not, even the disc harrow can destroy both docks and thistles if it is used thoroughly enough. The discs must be used alone and not in conjunction with the plough. I have destroyed a complete carpet of thistles by repeated discing until the young thistles were reduced each time almost to pulp. Docks can similarly be destroyed by cutting up the growing crown, while it still grows, leaving the root to decay in the ground. It is when the dock is brought to the *surface* by *ploughing* and then cut into pieces with the disc harrow that it is multiplied.

Of course, the safest and surest way with docks is the sheer hard labour of pulling or digging—a costly job these days.

PERSICARIA or RED-SHANK is another weed that makes good silage—and mowing once before it seeds will get rid of it. I have used and eliminated persicaria in two ways: by sowing oats and vetches and cutting the mixture of oats, vetches and persicaria for silage, just before the persicaria seeds; and by using the persicaria as a green manure on an unsown field—i.e. allowing it to grow to a leafy stage then discing it in as a green manure—repeating the operation three times between April and September. The same treatment is effective with FAT HEN.

CHARLOCK, though it is a nuisance in a corn crop, makes good silage for milk cows—especially mixed with lucerne or vetches; and it can easily be controlled by taking a silage crop. I have even rid a field of charlock, which swamped out a crop of kale, by cutting it and carting it to the cows in place of kale. In autumn, before they have tasted the real kale, they will eat it wilted—though they won't readily come back to it after kale.

Weeds, like CHICKWEED and GROUNDSEL, have provided me with thousands of tons of green manure for discing in between crops, and being annuals they rarely become a nuisance.

The tendency to destroy all weeds indiscriminately, especially by means of poison sprays, is a policy of despair now that the buckrake and green crop loader have made silage-making—a sure method of controlling weeds—so easy. Good husbandry surely demands a more intelligent study of the utilization and control of these sources of fertility and health.

I am continuing on my present farm experiments on weed utilization and control begun at Goosegreen—and I may say that I start with a wonderful array of well-established crops of many varieties!

On my present farm I have had some grand opportunities to demonstrate the process which uses weeds for the purpose of organic top-soil fertility building and at the same time cleaning a very dirty field.

I have in fact made a virtue out of the fact that my farm was in a very weedy state as well as low in fertility when I took it over; and I am using the weeds to build fertility, and in the same process clean each field.

When a dirty field is to be re-seeded, or cropped in any way, my procedure before cropping is to give it a weed-mulch fallow which builds fertility by *using* the weeds in the process of eliminating them.

If it is friable enough to work up enough soil with the disc harrows or rotary hoe only, I churn up the whole field with either or both. On some occasions I have preceded the disc harrows with a cultivator. But if the ground is hard and all the weeds cannot effectively be cut without the plough then the whole field will have to be ploughed just once; but not more than five inches deep—just enough to cut all weed roots and turn them over. Then all subsequent cultivations, throughout a full summer fallow, are done with the disc harrow or rotavator.

Instead of repeated ploughing to prevent any further weed growth from developing, I allow the weeds to grow up to the flowering stage, when they have produced their maximum bulk; then I use them as a green manure, discing them thoroughly into the top soil. The contribution which a disced-in weed crop makes to soil fertility is beyond all chemical analysis.

After the first weeds are disced in, the field is left untouched again for about a month or six weeks, The weeds again grow up to produce a further substantial green-manure crop, which is again disced in before any seed is set. These operations are repeated several times, allowing the weeds to grow: sometimes to their full maturity, to provide, when they are disced in, a large tonnage of bulky organic matter to improve the friability and water-holding capacity of the top soil; sometimes discing in when the growth is lush and green and at a high level of protein content, to add large quantities of nitrogen to the soil. Either way the weeds are always disced in before they go to seed. This results in the destruction of all weeds in the top few inches of soil—for what is missed in one discing is caught in the next and each time that the field rests, and growth is allowed, more un-germinated weed seeds germinate and grow and are disced into the soil before they can establish, unless seed is brought from outside by birds and wind.

But the field is never ploughed again before being sown. This would only bring up dormant weed seeds and put the now clean humus-rich top-soil down to the level where anaerobic conditions operate, making it quite useless to the crop that is to be sown.

But left unturned, with the destroyed weeds incorporated with the top soil, the soil begins to emulate the hedgerow conditions. The decaying weeds release organic acids in the process of decay, and the acids in turn dissolve the essential minerals which are nearly always present in every type of soil—but not always available or soluble until the acids of decaying organic matter make them so.

The action of aerobic nitrifying bacteria gathers nitrogen from the air to supplement the nitrogen directly supplied by the crop of green weeds. Thus, instead of dissolving the weeds in a deadly spray the consequences of which we cannot measure in destruction of ultimate fertility and human life, we have used the weeds to gain vast quantities of organic manure, and, in the process, left the field virtually weed-free.

If it is felt that the field needs further cleaning, the first crop sown is a silage crop, which can be followed with a further short repeat of the weed-mulch fallow in the month or two after it is mown for silage in its green state.

CHAPTER VIII

Getting the Best from the Grazing

Very few farmers are nowadays so wasteful of their pastures that they allow complete free range for the cattle to wander over the whole of a field. Some kind of controlled grazing is practised by most farmers who grow carefully chosen temporary leys. But there seems to be no concensus of opinion in favour of any particular system.

I've tried many ways of rationing or controlling the grazing of my cattle and am quite sure that completely free range grazing is wasteful and inefficient. What happens when a herd of cows is turned into a field of grass at the optimum stage for grazing? The best of the grazing is finished in three or four days and both quality and quantity of grazing then declines rapidly day by day. The cows have far too much grass, and all the best of the grass during the first day or two of grazing, for they are naturally selective and, unlike a child who saves the almond icing until last, they select the best first. Thereafter they may not have enough, in total quantity, or of the most valuable ingredients. Plants in the hedgerows which are an essential supplement of a simple ley mixture of shallow-rooted ingredients are also quickly eaten down. On the other hand, though more efficient quantity control can be achieved by rationing out the grazing by confining the cows to small sections of the field in rotation, or by allowing them a new strip each day, I would *not* advocate anything but uncontrolled grazing of *simple* mixtures if they are to be the sole pasturage. Close confinement on grazing which provides *only* a few ingredients is the most certain way of ensuring deficiency diseases and bloat, especially where access to the hedgerow herbs is not possible. Cattle which are confined by strip grazing on a small area of a heavily chemicalized growth of one or two shallow rooting grasses and a clover, will ingest large quantities of protein and yield large quantities of milk; but they are certain also to bring large quantities of trouble to the farmer, fees to the veterinary surgeon, and profits to the manufacturers of synthetic trace elements, and magnesium (and other) injections. The top soil of most agriculturally 'progressive' countries is so seriously deficient in the micro-elements of healthy and abundant production that to stimulate high yields, whilst confining the cow to a diet derived only from this inadequate top soil, is financial suicide for the farmer.

Controlled grazing is therefore likely to be trouble-free only if the mixtures used approximate in variety to those advocated in this book. I have, for many years, limited the area upon which my cows graze at any one time, but the variety of their diet, and the depth of mineral, and trace-element-rich subsoil from which it has been derived, have been unlimited. Always, where the complex herbal ley has been used the controlled grazing has been completely trouble free.

The fact that the *area* of grazing is limited does not mean that the total *quantity* is inadequate over the grazing period. Indeed the total production of herbage is considerably increased, for, as I have shown earlier, nothing stimulates growth more than grazing or mowing before the flowering stage. Frequent grazing down of young herbage, resting, grazing again, and repeating the process throughout the season, results in anything up to double the yield of herbage that would be obtained by the customary grazing over the whole field of near-mature herbage. What happens is that the cow on controlled grazing actually eats an increased total quantity of higher quality herbage spread evenly day by day over the whole grazing period.

Systems of controlled grazing which I have used are (see diagrams on pages 65-67):

1. *The On-and-Off system* in which the cattle go into a pasture at the ideal grazing stage for limited periods during the day but are made to lie back to a bare pasture.

2. *Rotational Paddock Grazing.* Dividing the field into limited areas but allowing the cattle to remain continuously on each paddock until the quality and quantity of herbage is inadequate before moving on to a fresh paddock.

3. *Strip-grazing across a whole field* by putting an electric fence across a field to provide a restricted strip of grazing, and moving the fence back each day to allow a strip of fresh herbage each day.

4. *Strip-grazing of limited paddocks.* In this system the field is divided by an electric fence into small paddocks and each paddock is strip-grazed by moving back each day an electric fence across each paddock.

System 4, in theory, makes the most efficient use of the grazing with the least amount of daily labour. The initial length of electric fencing is the greatest by this method and the daily labour is rather less than system 3 as the length of fence to be moved back is less and there is no back fence to be moved. So this could by many be considered the most productive method of utilizing the grazing. But after trying it for a short time I decided that the cattle were too closely confined and the dung deposited seemed to be much more concentrated than by any other method.

This resulted in considerable wastage of grazing on the second or third time round the paddocks. By the third grazing such a large proportion of the grass had been soiled by dung that much of the herbage was not acceptable to the cattle. Additionally I could not feel that such close concentration of cattle on a narrow strip of an already limited paddock was a good thing for the health of the cattle—even though a large variety of herbs was included in the mixtures.

I should have no hesitation in condemning this extreme limitation of grazing area on a ley of few ingredients. I have seen much trouble with indigestion, sterility, and worms, where this has been done on the simple ley.

System 1. Obviously the idea of allowing the cow to fill her stomach then lie down, chew the cud and make milk, was a good one. So I practised the on-and-off system for a long time, moving the cows on to an old pasture as soon as the quicker eaters—usually the better milkers—were satisfied. The sign for the whole herd to be moved was when a few of them started to lie down. About forty-five minutes on a good pasture was usually long enough.

But the disadvantages of this system were: (1) The cattle grew to realize they would be removed from the good pasture to a bare pasture and attempted too quickly to get their fill before being removed.

This resulted in over-eating and bloat. Leisurely eating is essential for a milking cow if she is to make the best use of her food. Rapid stuffing results in indigestion and incomplete utilization of food. Also of the utmost importance is the psychological effect on the cow. The cow who knows she can eat and drink at leisure, as much as she wants, when she wants, and choose her own intervals for lying down and chewing the cud, always makes better use of the food she eats than the cow who is rushed from one place to another, being compelled to grab her food during the limited regulation hours of a man-made schedule.

(2) Labour costs are increased by the need to move the cows from one field to another.

System 3. Strip-grazing across the whole field does not have the same disadvantage of confining the cows to such a limited area as System 4. But this system needs more labour to move a front fence forward to provide fresh grazing, and a back fence behind the cows to prevent the cows from over-grazing the grazed strips and stopping fresh growth.

The maintenance of an ever-ready water supply is a difficulty of this system. A portable water trough with a ball-tap is now available which can be wheeled forward to each fresh strip, but a very long hose is needed to maintain the supply of water from the main.

System 2. Rotational paddocks. This system has proved, in my experience, to be the easiest to operate, and the most efficient in total yield of herbage consistent with the production, health, and comfort of the cow. The field is divided into paddocks providing in each approximately one acre to each ten cows to be grazed. The field remains divided in this way throughout the season so that once the division fences have been erected no futher time is needed for fence moving. All that is needed is for the entrance wire to be moved to allow access to the paddock being grazed whilst leaving a passage to the water-trough but no access to the recently grazed or the fresh forward paddocks.

The ideal method of using this system is to allow young calves and their nurse cows to have first turn in each fresh paddock, followed by the milking herd, and last of all the heifers and dry cows. After the dry cows we top off any ungrazed herbage and let it lie. Whenever possible dung is spread with a flexible-tined scratcher on the tractor hydraulic lift. The reason for preceding the milking herd with the youngest stock is so that they shall get an adequate supply of minerals, trace elements, and vitamins, before any selective grazing has been done by the cows. This provision of best grazing for the calves is most important with pastures of simple mixtures. With a really complex herbal ley it is not so essential.

Alternatively, separate fields may be used for calves as well as dry cows. But it is wise also to divide these fields with the electric fence and essential that the mixture should contain the deep-rooting herbs, so important in laying the foundations of health for the calves.

ROTATIONAL PADDOCK GRAZING

Variations in Paddock divisions according to position of water supply

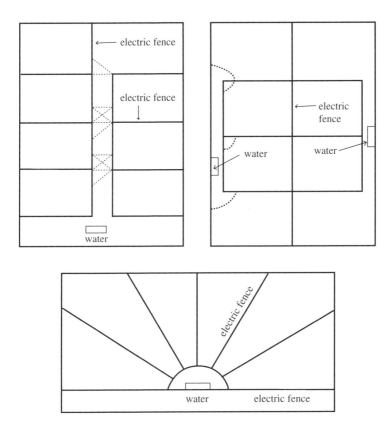

No fence moving is required for this system except to open and close
each paddock and allow access to water trough.

PADDOCK STRIP-GRAZING

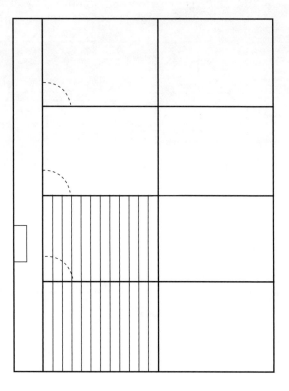

Field divided into paddocks, further movable fence placed across the field and moved back each day. No necessity for back fence as cattle move to next paddock when each paddock has been cleared in strips allowing each paddock time to grow before it is needed again.

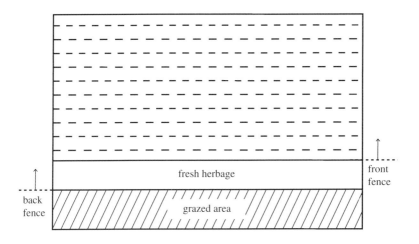

STRIP-GRAZING

Electric fence moved back each day followed by a 'back fence' which keeps the cows from roaming back or continuously grazing the new growth on the grazed area. This allows fresh growth behind the back fence.

ON-AND-OFF GRAZING

Cows graze free
range over whole
field for one hour
morning and night

Lie back field
(old pasture)

REARING CALVES ON ROUGHAGE

Calves in my herd live entirely on the fresh green herbage of the herbal ley (apart from the milk which they suckle from the cow), or in winter the silage made from that herbage. No other feeding is given (except an occasional feed of hay when we make it—mostly for experimental purposes only these days—until the heifer comes into the milking herd after calving her first calf. Even then food in addition to pasturage or silage does not exceed 1 lb. per gallon of milk yield.

The calves are turned out with nurse cows as soon after calving as they are settled with the nurse cow. Each calf has a week or ten days with its own dam to give it a really good start. Then it goes to a nurse cow (with one or more other calves) from which it receives 5-7 lb. of milk daily plus silage in winter, or grass, clover, and herbs in summer. The rest of the calf's life is spent out of doors—grazing in summer and self-feeding silage in winter.

I am listing below the names and yields of cows and heifers at present in the herd reared from birth by this method. Their yields, obtained almost entirely on grazing and silage, indicate the efficiency of such a dietary. I am not suggesting that cows reared on substitutes from birth and concentrates from an early age, will, if changed to my natural feeding system, immediately adapt themselves sufficiently to yield milk so efficiently. But there is no doubt about the efficiency of the system of summer grazing and winter self-service feeding, where the animal has been accustomed to it from birth as the following home-bred animals have. These, their current lactations, are a fair sample of the system.

Name	Yield lbs.	Days	Butter-fat	Calf
Polden Pilot's Pearl....	10,250	343	5.5	1st
Polden Chocolate Cake...	8,332½	335	5.73	1st
Polden Mogulla's Sultana...	9,344½	358	5.78	2nd
Polden Patrician Springtime...	8,399½	313	5.17	2nd
Polden Miss Mannin...	7,842	283	5.97	2nd
Polden Sunrise...	8,860¼	331	5.14	3rd
Polden Morning Mist...	7,754½	292	5.72	3rd
Polden Sunwise...	9,450½	364	5.45	4th
Polden Haughty Hetty...	13,140½	364	5.75	7th
Polden Dolly Daydream...	13,881	363	5.15	3rd

CHAPTER IX

Making the Ley with a Mower

I wonder how many thousands of pounds have been wasted by farmers following 'expert' advice, since the first fertilizer salesman, masquerading as a Ministry of Agriculture advisory officer, inflicted his theoretical knowledge on a farmer?

I often feel glad that I have had the courage to resist most of the advice offered to me, when it has had a recommendation for some commercial by-product of industry wrapped up in it. And, when I have *not* ignored the advice—and I am ready to listen to advice from any man of practical experience—I have at least passed it through a very fine sieve of sceptical Yorkshire caution. In this way I've garnered a lot of useful knowledge, discovered a lot about the subtle sales-methods of the chemical combines, and saved myself a lot of money which might otherwise have been washed down those tile drains of my fields that were not blocked by my predecessors' losses.

It is generally claimed in orthodox official agricultural circles that it is not possible to establish a good ley without the use at least of phosphatic fertilizers and lime, but preferably plus potassic fertilizers or a 'complete' manure as well. Some experts will admit that a reasonable organic content in the soil might be useful to help in moisture-holding until the ley is established—but by far the greater majority of ley farming experts completely ignore organic matter when advising on the establishment of a good ley. I have searched all the books I know that deal with this subject, and in every case organic manures in the establishment of the ley are mentioned only in a very secondary way.

In every case phosphates are considered absolutely essential, as is lime on acid soils. In all cases, except one, nitrogenous fertilizers are considered important.

In *my* experience the *only* essential is organic matter. The use of adequate organic manure, which need not necessarily include animal wastes (though they improve its effectiveness) will, on all soils, ensure the release of all other requirements of the ley. Organic nitrogen, phosphates, potash, even calcium in small but usually adequate quantities, are supplied in the process of decomposition of organic matter.

Synthetic nitrogen is indeed harmful, and in the extent to which it is used the successful establishment of a good clover sward is made more difficult. I am proud to know that my experience in this respect is confirmed by that very honest and well supported ley farming authority, Sir George Stapledon. Writing at the outset of the last war (before the official pressure for the excessive use of nitrogenous fertilizers had begun to rob farmers of their soil fertility, though I am convinced that Sir George was too brave to be intimidated by official government policy), he said in *Ley Farming* (Faber & Faber): 'All crops respond to nitrogen, but there is a real risk of the soluble nitrogenous manures reacting adversely on sustained soil fertility when applied to land that is out of heart, devoid of humus. . . .

'The risk to be guarded against with nitrogen is that its use will tend to drain the soil of other essential elements and that it will decrease fertility in proportion to its contribution to the bulk of any crop wholly or in major part removed from the farm.

'Thus there is some considerable danger in an over-insistence on top-dressing cereals, and especially wheat, and indeed on an over-insistence on a general use of nitrogen without regard to soil conditions and the wider implications of the manner of soluble nitrogenous fertilizers.'

Sir George Stapledon and I are also in the good company of a greater farmer than either of us, Robert H. Elliot, whose book, *Clifton Park System of Farming,* in spite of some important limitations and an outdated objection to ryegrass, is still the best basic book on ley farming. In this book he says: 'Landlord's capital mainly consists of soil, *and the condition of the soil mainly depends on the amount of humus it contains.* About 100 years ago Scottish agricultural capital was on a sound footing, because the system pursued maintained the humus of the soil. It is in an unsound condition now [and this applies to most British and American soil to-day—F. N. T.] because from continuous liming and the use of artificial manures the humus of the soil has immensely declined (hence the numerous complaints of the exhaustion of the soil), and is declining steadily except in those rare cases [very much rarer now!—F. N. T.] where enough farmyard manure can be obtained to keep up the supply of humus.'

'The object of my farming system at Clifton-on-Bowmont is to show how Scottish agriculture may be restored to its originally sound position—not only to replace, but to steadily increase, the humus of the soil, and render the farmer, as he once was, *independent of the use of artificial manures.* In other words, my farming system is directed to restoring the capital of the landlord to its originally sound and safe position, to lessen the expenditure at present required by the tenant, and place all his crops in a safe position, for contending at once against foreign competition and vicissitudes of climate . . .'

But there, with Robert Elliot and Sir George Stapledon, alone among ley-farming authors and advocates, insistence on organic matter and the dangers of fertilizers stops. Can anyone imagine any modern chemically-controlled Ministry of Agriculture identifying its objects with those of Robert Elliot, who, let it be admitted, is no opponent of the use of chemicals, for he says 'these may still be used under certain circumstances to a moderate extent.' Yet where is the official adviser who can free himself from commercial ties and, with his Minister's backing, join Robert Elliot in saying 'the object of our advice is to steadily increase the humus of the soil and render the farmer independent of artificial fertilizers?'

Organic matter is the *one* essential of successful herbal ley establishment and, once established, the herbal ley is itself the best builder of humus, and thus fertility, in the soil, and healthy productivity in the animal.

Ignorance or denial of this fact must be costing the British farmer colossal sums of money in wasted and unnecessary expenditure. For I am quite sure the fact that organic matter is the one and only essential of good ley establishment is not included in the advice of the experts.

The following example of my own experience must be typical of many other farms. Fortunately I had used enough observation in the study and practice of ley farming to know how seriously to take orthodox advice.

Approximately twenty acres of the twenty-eight acres of my field known as Burlons Drove East was seeded down with a herbal ley, in the following manner, in September. The field, being extremely weedy and terribly poor, was summer-fallowed, then sown in July to mustard. It was in such poor heart that the mustard did not make more than about three inches growth before it was disced in during early September. No manures, either organic or inorganic were used. We had no organic manure on the farm (for I was responsible for this seeding before actually taking over the farm on my own, i.e. while I was still at Goosegreen, before moving to Ferne, I had the opportunity to crop some of the Ferne land and Burlons Drove East was one field thus cropped).

After discing in the small crop of mustard, the herbal ley mixture, as follows, was sown with a seed barrow:

> 5 lb. S.23 Perennial Ryegrass
> 5 lb. Commercial Perennial Ryegrass
> 5 lb. Cocksfoot S.26
> 2 lb. Chicory
> 2 lb. Burnett
> 2 lb. Sheep's Parsley
> 2 lb. Kidney Vetch
> 2 lb. S.100 White Clover
> 1 lb. Alsike
> 2 lb. American Sweet Clover
> 2 lb. Lucerne

It was very slow to break ground and went through the winter in a poor thin condition. It was again very slow to start in the spring and it soon became evident that the many weeds, which we hoped the fallow—though a wet one—had destroyed, were gaining control again. I turned the heifers in during April, hoping that they would help to control the weeds and encourage the root development and ultimate establishment of the ingredients of the ley. The weeds grew away from the heifers; they grazed half-heartedly the patches of mainly ryegrass, and to the orthodox eye it was evident that the ley was a failure. In fact when the agricultural committee experts did a survey of the farm in June, that was their verdict.

At that time the ryegrass was about half a crop, there was no clover, a leaf of chicory here and there; but a thick mat of mayweed, thistles and spurrey, all poor-fertility and acidity weeds, covered the whole field. I had a soil-analysis which showed phosphates low, potash normal and pH only 5.5. In other words, on orthodox standards, the ley had failed because I had omitted the orthodox essentials for establishing a pasture—phosphates and lime. It was indeed a pale and sorry sight, and I asked the agricultural committee experts what they advised me to do.

'Well, if you mow what's there, you'll get a bit of hay from the ryegrass to help out your losses and give you a little winter feed. Do that, then plough up the field and give it a summer fallow, ploughing as often as possible through the rest of the summer to try and get rid of the infestation of weeds. Then sow a green crop that can be grazed off with sheep or ploughed in, give a heavy dressing of complete fertilizer with the green crop and re-sow the ley next spring, with sulphate of ammonia to give it a good start.'

'Wouldn't it be robbing an already very poor field to carry this bit of hay off?' I said. 'Maybe,' was the reply, 'but you must use enough fertilizer to make that good.'

In view of the low pH I had already ordered three tons an acre of ground chalk to be spread. What would the additional cost of the committee advice amount to?

	£	2006* £	$
Plough twenty acres say three times for an orthodox fallow	80	1,952	3,592
Seed for greencrop	20	488	898
Sowing	10	244	449
Complete Fertilizer—£8 (£189*) an acre	160	3,904	7,184
Sulphate of Ammonia	40	976	1,796
Lime	60	1,464	2,694
Re-seeding of ley Cultivations	30	732	1,347
Herbal ley seed at £8 (£189*) an acre	160	3,904	7,184
Sowing	10	244	449
Harrowing or rolling in	20	488	898
	£590	14,397	26,491

*Editor's note: The author's historic financial data was converted to modern currencies and approximately adjusted for inflation, using the consumer price index. This most certainly will not correlate to modern costs and prices, but should be utilized for general directional trends only.

Now this must sound, even to orthodox ears, a colossal sum for the establishment of a twenty-acre ley. But it is only fair to say that it must be taken as a somewhat extravagant effort to reclaim a very poor field, and it was assumed no doubt by the advisers that considerable benefit would accrue in the increased production of the ley and subsequent crops, to offset a large proportion of the expenditure on fertilizers. On the other hand, from my point of view, there could be no guarantee of that—and of course it also assumes that there is no cheaper means of getting the ley established and the field into good heart and production.

The fact is, and this is the whole point of this chapter, I turned this apparent failure into one of the best leys in the county, merely by giving it a feed of its own growth, without a penny of expenditure other than wages, fuel and wear and tear on the mowing machine. I did not gather the bit of hay that was growing there—that would have been banditry of my own future from a field so poor. I did not even apply the three tons an acre of ground chalk which was ordered for the field; for at the time chalk was being spread on the rest of the farm, we were mowing this particular field, and I asked the contractor to leave it until later (and the subsequent fine fettle of the ley made me postpone the application indefinitely). merely mowed the mixture of weeds and ryegrass with the swatheboard off, so that they spread evenly over the ground. What was mown was then left to lie there as a surface mulch. I merely fed back to a very hungry field its own growth, and when there was a second growth through it in August—incidentally when grazing elsewhere was very scarce—I turned all the heifers and dry cattle into it and let them graze it hard. By the end of August it was evident that clovers, chicory and grasses were establishing and spreading rapidly, after the much-needed feed of organic matter and the obvious release of mineral nutrients resulting from the partial decay of the mown weeds and ryegrass.

In September the cattle were moved; and a short growth of clover and chicory, topped off and left to lie again in green high-protein condition, gave a stimulating free kick of nitrogen which clinched the completion of a first-class ley.

With further winter grazing, by March of the following year it was clear that we had a ley that was without superior in Britain. The many visitors, to whom I have not failed to tell the story of the ley that I saved for nothing and kept £600 in my pocket, will confirm my claim to any of the parrots who echo: 'You can't make a good ley without phosphates and lime': who have never tried to make one with adequate organic matter and a mower. And 95 percent of these visitors who have marvelled at this ley have been thoroughly orthodox followers of the poison-powder merchants, including three violently sceptical (but thinking hard when they left my farm) Young Farmers' Clubs, the Agricultural Attaché of a great agricultural country who admitted the superiority of my ley but said to a mutual friend later: 'That man's *feet* make fertility anyhow—he'd farm just as well if he used chemicals—but it might cost him a lot more!'; and many a heavy user of chemicals who wished they had as productive a ley on their farms.

By the time this book is published this ley will be in its third year—but it will still be producing more than any field on similar or better soil conditions in the district. In this, its second year, it supplied over 200 tons of silage, 10 tons of high-protein tripod hay, and most of the grazing for 25 cows, which produced between March and October, with the addition of only 3 tons of dredge corn, £2,800 worth of milk (wholesale prices).

And on analysis, this soil, without addition of a single chemical fertilizer, is no longer phosphate- or calcium-deficient.

On what knowledge or experience did I use the above method of building this ley, instead of taking the expert advice to rip it up and start again at such great cost? For many years I have taken every opportunity, after each grazing of the leys, to top off the surplus grass. Now the orthodox reason for this topping after grazing, quite commonly advised of course, is to stop the seeding stems and encourage a fresh leafy growth. But with the herbal ley, though an important reason for topping off, it is not *the* most valuable contribution which is made to the subsequent development and production of the ley. For the surplus, after grazing a herbal ley, consists of a considerable proportion of deep-rooting herbs; and these deep-rooting herbs have been down to the subsoil to bring to their stems and leaves a rich supply of minerals, trace-elements and who knows what, which are not available in the top soil to the shallow-rooting ingredients of the orthodox simple mixture of only grasses and clovers.

I soon discovered with the herbal ley, that the benefit resulting from the use of the mower after grazing was obviously far greater than the mere encouragement of leaf growth. It seemed possible that the contribution to soil fertility and the subsequent nutrition of the crop from the feeding-back of this ungrazed surplus was quite considerable. So I decided to develop the practice deliberately as a process of feeding the ley—in other words free fertilizer from the subsoil instead of the usual synthetic top dressing; topping off instead of top dressing. And I found in this way that I could maintain, entirely by utilizing free natural processes, the high production of the ley.

I will explain what happens.

A ley which is grazed mainly by cows, which depend on it almost entirely for the maintenance of their milk output, needs—according to the orthodox soil chemist—phosphates, potash, calcium and nitrogen. It needs—according to me—plant hormones, trace elements, mycelia and fungi, organic acids and a 'stomach-full' of bulky roughage. Additionally I believe optimum growth demands the soil temperature which can only be maintained at an even level by the heat generated from the aerobic bacterial activity which takes place in the presence of decaying organic matter and free air. This means surface organic matter—not ploughed-in organic matter, which cannot do its work below air-level in the soil because of lack of oxygen and atmospheric nitrogen. The optimum temperature for growth and bacterial activity lasts for only a very short period during the summer in soils here the organic content is low, because it is maintained only by external warmth. This explains the wide variations month by month in the soil analyses quoted in Chapter VI on *Natural Crop Nutrition*. But in a top soil where the level of organic matter continues high—or better still is frequently raised by a surface mulch of short mowings of grasses, clovers and herbs—the variations in the availability of essential nutrients in the top soil is very small, which means that the variation from ideal growing conditions is very small. So that the growing-season of the ley is considerably longer than on the ley managed in the orthodox way: with little or no feeding back of its own growth, but instead frequent bacteria-depressing, temperature-reducing applications of sulphate of ammonia or nitro-chalk. But the scientist may well ask, what has this to do with the supply of those all-important phosphates? Well, it's the story I've told so often before, of availability. The decay of the mowing mulch releases the organic acids which release the locked-up phosphates. And so, the flow of what I consider an almost unlimited supply of phosphates in most soils (I won't be so dogmatic as to say *all* soils because I cannot be sure of that, though it may well be), is kept in motion so long as *some* decaying organic matter is maintained on or near title top soil. *I have never known a phosphate problem in a soil where there is ample organic matter*; and that need not necessitate the application of compost or farmyard manure, though it may be desirable on seriously overcropped or thin soils. It merely means that some decaying vegetation should be made available on the soil surface—or at deepest in the top three inches—and added to at every reasonably convenient opportunity. All needful phosphates will then be rendered soluble to maintain all the phosphate requirements of the most heavily grazed of pastures. And I have yet to see the soil in which there is insufficient phosphate (albeit insoluble and temporarily unavailable until the acids of decay dissolve it) for this to be done. If any doubter can show me such a soil, I will show him how to grow on it a first-class clover-thick pasture, without an ounce of basic slag, superphosphate, sulphate of ammonia or any other soluble chemical.

16. Grazing the 'fertility pastures' in electrically-fenced paddocks.

17. Waiting to be let into the electrically-fenced paddocks, in the passage between nine paddocks in an eighteen-acre field.

18. The author's herd; heads down to fertility pastures. Note the capacious udders and big bellies to utilize high-quality natural food.

19. Some of the herd crossing a recently topped-off paddock.

I shall describe in the next chapter another way in which I did this on land which the most reasonable and moderate of expert opinion considered impossible without applying phosphates in some inorganic form.

As far as the potash needs of the ley are concerned, that is never a problem on the fully stocked and properly grazed pasture. Animal dung and urine, in combination with nature's best potash manufacturer, the earthworm, will maintain a potash level in all soils, higher than the maximum needs of any pasture or subsequent arable crop in a sensible rotation. Potash deficiencies are only created by the unbalancing effect of the excessive use of soluble nitrogenous fertilizers. In turn the attempt to correct this artificially-created potash deficiency by the use of inorganic potassic manures, immediately upsets the magnesium balance in the soil, and a worse deficiency for the dairy farmer resulting in the mysterious collapse of his cows shortly after calving. No dairy farmer need worry about potash deficiency; but if he is persuaded to use potassic supers, or sulphate of potash or any other soluble potassic fertilizer, he had better be prepared for the far bigger headache of magnesium deficiency in his cattle.

Faced with either a potash or magnesium deficiency, and quick results are needed, apply seaweed fertilizer which is entirely organic and specially rich in these two elements. If the necessary passage of time required for a natural adjustment—by methods described earlier—can be allowed, no purchased manure of any kind need be used. Incidentally, seaweed fertilizer is the answer to any trace-element deficiency which needs immediate solution. Use it on the ley as a top-dressing in conjunction with a natural seaweed mineral mixture provided *ad lib.* in troughs for the cows. *Synthetic* trace-elements or mineral mixtures can be very dangerous, for though a trace-element is essential to life in natural context and infinitesimal proportions it becomes lethal when taken in the smallest synthetic excess. Provided in natural organic form it cannot possibly do any harm. The only really natural form is in the leaves of the deep-rooting ingredients of the herbal ley; or, until the herbal leys are well established by feeding powdered mixture of dried seaweeds and mineral rich herbs. If you use either or both these natural sources of trace-elements you need never fear 'grass staggers' in your cattle or sheep.

CHAPTER X

Making a Ley with Sawdust Compost

From 1946 to 1948 I worked in Eire, reclaiming the poorest farm I've ever seen, even among the barren areas of that island of extremes. That farm in the hills of County Wick-low couldn't carry a single worm in its thin, farmed-out slopes. I scratched and dug in every field of its 700 acres in search of the worms which would tell me which field could grow a crop while I tried to build the fertility of the rest. But there wasn't a worm to be found, except under stones in the kitchen garden, where some hens had set the soil fertility cycle in motion.

Taking a deep interest in my proposals for that farm—which incidentally were also the concern of the late Sir Albert Howard, who spent some time there with me and joined in the unsuccessful search for worms—was one of the most experienced and respected agricultural experts in Ireland, Dr. Henry Kennedy.

He shared with me the view that what the farm needed to restore its fertility, as did, and still do, vast areas of the rest of Ireland, was first-class leys and plenty of cattle to graze them. But the key to those fertility-forming pastures, said Dr. Kennedy, was phosphates. 'I agree with everything you say about restoring the fertility of that farm,' he said, 'but plus a little slag! You'll never grow clover there without basic slag. Get the cycle started with phosphates and you can go on and make it fertile by organic methods thereafter.' And of course, as far as orthodox experience and knowledge had then gone, that was a very sober argument. And coming from such an authority as Dr. Kennedy no one in Ireland would have thought of questioning it. Certainly no one had had the courage to try an alternative system against it. But though I was the 'new boy' in Ireland, who dared to question this argument, I felt I was an old hand in England at establishing a fertile pasture. I had already made many acres of first-class leys, on phosphate-deficient soils, entirely by organic methods.

So, though I may then have appeared to be disrespectful of an expert Irish authority (I may say I acquired considerable respect and admiration for Dr. Kennedy in the years that followed—though not for his slag!) I told him I would grow good leys with plenty of clover and I would use no slag or other chemical manures. And in three years from scratch we had established the best leys that had ever been seen in that district; and I believe with the foreman who had worked on that farm for thirty years— 'the best in the whole of the Emerald Oile!'

This is what we did:

I decided that the best crop to start the fertility-building process and to produce an income at the same time, without taking anything out of the soil, would be sugar beet. It was quite a remunerative crop at that time and had the advantage of not robbing the soil. Indeed its deep roots would start immediately to tap the subsoil to bring minerals and trace elements to the beet leaves which were later to be added to the top soil when they were disced in. So far from robbing the soil, it added to it by utilizing it to a greater depth than any other cash crop. The cultivation and organic manuring necessary to get a good crop of sugar beet provided a wonderful opportunity to clean the field and lay good foundations for the establishment of the temporary pasture.

Sugar-beet growing also gave us the right to draw, from the sugar-beet factory, pulp, which was in great demand and for which priority was given to growers. By getting all the pulp back from our own beet, and by feeding the tops on, or discing them in, all that would be taken off the field was the very small proportion of sugar in the crop, as well, of course, as moisture (which in Ireland is in plentiful supply from the skies, so we were quite well able to spare that!). The subsoil minerals raised by the roots and deposited in the leaves were ample recompense for removal of the sugar.

The first step—whatever the state of the land or the previous crop (or half-crop, as was then the case on that farm)—was to prepare a seed bed and clean the land. Where my weed-mulch fallow was possible in the summer preceding cropping with beet, this was taken—but in most cases we wished to get straight into cropping and so we only had the autumn, winter and early spring to prepare the ground.

So autumn ploughing was the first step. The ground was not friable enough, except on one small field that had the summer fallow, to prepare it by discing only. If we had had the rotary hoe in those days, that would have been the tool for all operations. But we ploughed just deep enough to turn everything over, without putting it so deep that we lost the benefit of such vegetation as there was, to the top soil. Then we disced periodically as the furrows greened over with growth.

Three tons an acre of ground limestone were then spread.

Meantime a major operation of compost-making was in progress. A five-ton lorry was engaged almost continuously hauling farmyard manure from the many heaps that official propaganda had persuaded local farmers was hardly worth the trouble while they could buy chemical manures. Indeed, one small farmer thanked a friend of mine who was buying farmyard manure in another part of Ireland and said: 'This money will enable me to buy some artificials.'

On farm after farm in the neighbourhood were large dung-heaps which had accumulated over the years—in many cases overgrown with weeds to become a baby mountain in the middle of the farm, serving no other purpose than to train the rooster and his 'chirpers' for an 'Everest expedition!' And these heaps I bought for a few kind words and the joy of seeing them moved to make way for more.

At the nearby forestry department of a large estate was also fifty years' accumulation of sawdust, much of it black and rotted; this we had for the fetching.

Mixed in layers alternately with bracken (of which we had large quantities on totally neglected parts of the farm) and farmyard manure, gave us perfect materials for starting the cycle which Dr. Kennedy was adamant could only be started with basic slag.

We built our compost-heaps in sections 10 ft. square, rising to a height of 6 ft. and in layers which were roughly as follows:

> At the base: 10 in. of bracken
> > then: 10 in. of fairly green farmyard manure
> > 3 in. of sawdust
> > A sprinkle over the whole of ground limestone
> > 3 in. of bracken
> > 3 in. of F Y M
> > 3 in. of sawdust
> > A sprinkle of ground limestone

and repeating 3 inches bracken, 3 inches F Y M, 3 inches sawdust, a sprinkling of ground limestone, until the desired height was reached, then topping off with sawdust.

The heap was built lightly, as far as possible without being walked on— so that ample air was incorporated to allow the necessary aerobic bacterial activity to develop and to avoid the necessity to turn the heap. Sufficient air was incorporated during the building of the heap, without causing the heap to become too dry, so it was not necessary to turn the heap at all. This is specially so when the finished compost is to be applied as a surface mulch, or just disced into the top soil, where, in the presence of ample air, atmospheric nitrogen, and moisture, the process of decomposition can continue. Indeed, I believe that by these methods it is better that the compost should better that the compost should *not* be completely mature at the time of application, so that the heat-generating and organic-acid-releasing process of decay can continue in the top soil to set free the insoluble minerals in the soil. It is most important that any compost containing sawdust should *not* be ploughed under. If it is, the soil is robbed of nitrogen necessary for the continuing decomposition of the sawdust, which can rarely be completely broken down in the compost-heap that is not turned. Spread on the top soil, and lightly incorporated in the top soil with disc harrow or rotary hoe, sufficient nitrogen is gathered from the atmosphere to operate the decomposition of *any* kind of sawdust. So keep sawdust-compost always on top and you cannot go wrong.

We added no moisture to the heap while building it, for in Ireland, as in England, sufficient rain falls in a normal year to provide adequate moisture for the heap.

After approximately six months in the heap we spread the compost on the disced field at the rate of fifteen tons an acre. (Remember that we were dealing with quite barren soil—I think ten tons an acre sufficient on normal soils.) Following the spreading of the compost we disced the field repeatedly to get it clean before drilling the sugar-beet seed in April.

No other manurial or fertilizer applications were made.

It cannot be said that we had an exceptional crop of sugar beet. This was not to be expected on such poor land; indeed the advisory officer of the beet factory was quite sure that without the fertilizer allocation specially permitted by government edict to all beet growers on signature of their acreage contract, we should not have a crop worth harvesting. We did not take up the fertilizer permit, though some neighbours cursed me for not taking it and selling the 'coupons' to them! The advisory officer tried to press me to use at least some potassic fertilizer, for he was sure the sugar content of the beet would be too low without it.

In fact, when the beet was harvested we had quite an average crop for the season; and in a season when sugar contents were well below average, our sugar content was well above the average and one of the best in that area for many years.

We left the beet tops on the field, ate off half with sheep and disced-in the other half. The sheep stayed continuously on the field, being folded across it, so that all their dung and urine went back to the field. The difference in subsequent crops (wheat then ley) between the section with tops disced in and that on which the sheep were folded was indistinguishable, so that in the consideration of relative fertility contribution between discing-in and eating-on, both methods are equal.

There would, of course, be the live weight gain of the sheep to show some financial advantage for the eating-on method; and I am satisfied that there would be an appreciable difference in subsequent crops in favour of eating the tops on the ground compared with *ploughing*-in, because the sugar-beet leaf would quickly putrefy and its manurial value be lost, if put underground out of reach of aerobic bacteria.

As soon as the whole field was disced after clearance of the sugar beet, winter wheat was sown. If sugar-beet harvesting was delayed or the folding of sheep took us too far into the winter to crop comfortably with winter wheat, the discing was repeated in the spring and spring wheat or oats sown.

No further manuring was done and the cereal crop, whether winter-or spring-sown, was undersown in May, with a grass seed fiddle, broadcasting a herbal ley mixture.

Our only difficulty, in the damp Irish Summer, was not to get the ley established, but that we had got the field in such good heart by the previous treatment, that the young grass, clover and herb plants established so quickly that they grew almost apace with the wheat; chicory and all became quite a problem in the wheat straw; but harvesting on tripods was the answer to that problem.

Once the grain crop was harvested there was no shadow of doubt about the ability of phosphate deficient, farmed-out land being capable of growing a good clover sward.

There were leys to make the Emerald Isle proud of her name; for with leys like this painted across Ireland, she could really begin to live up to her name. It doesn't need imported superphosphate or basic slag to change the pale green-grey colour of vast stretches of Irish pasture one sees in flying over Ireland. It merely needs the proper use of the organic resources already present on and around most farms. And if the Minister of Agriculture feels he must offer the farmer a magic powder to darken the colour of his bilious-looking pastures, then let him use the rich deposits of natural rock which are available by the million tons for the grinding; or the vast quantity of mineral-and-trace-element-rich seaweed thrown almost daily at his doorstep by a benevolent nature.

And what is true for Ireland is true for almost every country in the world.

CHAPTER XI

Establishing & Breaking the Ley

I suppose I ought to touch wood while saying that I have never yet had a failure in fifteen years of establishing leys. I very *nearly* had one, described in Chapter VIII, *Making a Ley with a Mower*, until I fed the field with what I am convinced is the one and only manurial secret of successful leys—an adequate supply of organic matter to the top soil. In considering the high proportion of failures which have been experienced by farmers, especially in the dryer areas of low rainfall, it is significant that organic matter is also the one essential which no official cropping expert or soil analyst ever advises, or measures, in his assessment of the needs of the soil when recommending to the farmer the chemical 'essentials' for the successful establishment of a pasture. If soil scientists would concern themselves with the organic content of the soil, and determine the minimum level essential to establish a ley, with no assistance whatever from artificial chemical aids, failures need never be, and expenditure on unnecessary fertilizers would be cut, while at the same time the life and productive ability of the ley would be greatly increased.

A good farmer does not, of course, need a soil analyst to tell him whether his soil contains enough organic matter: his own feet and hands can feel the answer for him, and the friability of the soil behind the disc harrow or rotavator plainly indicates the readiness of the soil to receive the seed. But if he wants outside advice, let him ask for a measurement of organic content rather than chemical recommendations. Organic matter is the one stable factor, the quantity of which does not vary greatly from one month to another. A chemical analysis on the other hand can vary widely from one week to the next, according to soil temperature, moisture, and bacterial activity. This week you may be advised to apply 10 cwt. of basic slag an acre. Next week the phosphate status of the field could be adequate with no need to spend a penny on purchased fertilizers. (See Chapter VI—*Natural Crop Nutrition.*)

86

So the preparation of the land for the ley requires, as its most valuable purpose, the building of the organic surface skin, into which the seed will be sown. And the place of the ley in the rotation should be at the point where the level of organic matter is at its highest. In my farming this is as soon as convenient after a dressing of farmyard manure or compost.

The type of rotation into which the ley will fit depends on the extent to which you will come with me in relying on the ley for the entire feeding of the herd, and the amount of cropping which is being practised for the sale of crops additional to the needs of the cattle.

If the cropping rotation is entirely for the feeding of cattle, whether for beef or milk production, then the ideal rotation is that described in Chapter V—*Self-feeding for the Soil.*

What is there described as a sectional re-seeding of one field, putting each section through the rotation, kale, vetch-oat mixture, seeds (ley), may be used in separate fields instead of separate sections of one field.

The rotation for maximum fodder production and soil fertility building is then:

> ALL-GREEN ROTATION:
> 1st year Kale
> 2nd year Vetch-oat mixture
> 3rd year Ley
> 4th year Ley
> 5th year Ley
> 6th year Ley
>   and to Kale again.

Farmyard manure or compost is applied for either the kale or the oat and vetch mixture, whichever happens at the time to be the most convenient. Each crop benefits equally well—both being gross feeders of organic manures in a less decomposed condition. Then, one or two seasons later, the manure applied for the kale or vetch mixture has decomposed and changed to humus to bring the soil to its optimum condition for the sowing of the ley.

This is a rotation that is specially beneficial in a dry climate, the only possible adaptation from any moister conditions being the use of a deeper-rooting, more drought-resistant crop in place of oat and vetch. For this purpose American Sweet Clover, Broad Red Clover, and Chicory would be ideal mixture; though few soils, however dry, will not grow more bulk of green food for silage from oat (or rye) and vetches than from any other crop, provided a dressing of organic manure can be given in the preparation of the seed bed—either for the oats and vetches mixture or the crop preceding it.

Where straw crops are needed for bedding straw and feeding, or dredge-corn for cattle, pigs and poultry, this all-green rotation is merely modified by the addition of one or two straw crops between the ley and the kale, the kale and the vetches, or between the vetch mixture and the ley. If the kale can be cleared by February, there is time to fit in a spring cereal crop before taking an autumn crop of oats and vetches. If that is not possible, then the vetches must be followed with an autumn cereal which will be undersown with the new ley in the following spring.

It is in our cultivations, in growing all other crops in the rotations, and in preparing for the ley that we effect great savings over the orthodox system, enabling us to spend that extra pound or two on the seeds mixture.

The only time we need use the plough—and in consequence the operations made necessary by the effect of the plough—is in breaking the ley; and with the introduction of the rotary hoe it is now only when the ley is too wet, or too dry and hard for it, that we need use a plough even to break the ley. As there is more latitude in tune for the breaking of the ley as compared with other crops, we can usually wait until the ground is in the right state for the rotary hoe before we break it. Though we are really concerned in this chapter with *establishing* the ley, now that I have referred to breaking the ley I may as well say here how that is done; for the process is so simple it will not take up much space to describe it.

We merely choose a day when there is a reasonably dry surface to the ley, after it has been grazed down bare. The rotary hoe then goes in at about an inch deep and skims off the turf. A second time over with the rotary hoe then cuts off another inch of soil to mix with the turf. Third time over, the depth is increased to four inches and the finished seed bed is then ready for either kale or cereal.

If the ley is sown with the oat and vetch mixture, or immediately the oat and vetch mixture has been sown, then usually once over the kale stubble with the rotary hoe is the only cultivation that is needed. A second stroke with the rotary hoe is in any case the maximum requirement on an oat and vetch stubble.

Using disc harrows twice over is sufficient on all except the roughest or heaviest of land.

When sown *with* the oat and vetch mixture we mix all the seeds together and sow with the grain drill. When the ley seeds are sown separately we use either the seed fiddle or seed barrow. I prefer the seed fiddle, which is by far the quickest way of sowing grass, clover and herb seeds, and (unless there is a strong wind when no attempt should be made to sow grass seeds at all except with a drill) it gives an even spread and avoids putting the seeds too deep.

The best way of covering the seed is with the roller. Indeed, if the ground is at all rough after discing or rotavating, once over with the ring roller is wise *before* sowing as well, especially if the sowing is to be done on foot with the seed fiddle or barrow.

Ley seeds must be left tightly embedded by the soil: and as both disc harrows and rotary hoe leave the soil rather too loose, rolling with either ring roll or flat roll is necessary as the final operation in sowing the ley.

Where the ley is to be sown direct after cereal or kale crop— without a companion or nurse crop like oats and vetches or a straight cereal crop— then I like to fit in a green-manuring crop to be disced or rotavated in before sowing the ley. This makes doubly sure of good soil structure, ample moisture and a good content of organic nitrogen, as well as the phosphates released slowly for the new ley seeds by the decomposing green crop.

American sweet clover or broad red clover are the best green legumes for this purpose if time allows for a good growth, i.e. eight or ten weeks. If there is not more than a month or six six weeks' margin of time before the need to sow the ley—then mustard is the quickest growing and cheapest green crop manure. But mustard does not gather atmospheric nitrogen, so should only be used when time is very limited; and that need not be often, for the kale will be out of the way by the end of March, and the ley does not have to be sown before late August or early September.

This means that the kale stubble can be worked and sown with the green crop in April; the green crop incorporated with the topsoil in late July or early August, leaving ample time to get the ley sown by the end of August if you are not too preoccupied with the struggle to save the cereal harvest.

Never plough in the green crop. Seventy-five percent of its value is lost by putting it right under where it will putrefy, instead of passing through a slow aerobic process of decomposition, assisted by oxygen-loving nitrifying bacteria which will prepare a warm and rich seed bed for the ley seeds. Ploughed under, the green crop is of no use to the ley seeds at all, and indeed, by the sponge-like action several inches under the soil, draws down the moisture that is needed on top to give the ley a good start. This is one of the greatest errors of the dry-land farmer. All his troubles and difficulties in ley establishment can be overcome by keeping the organic sponge on top.

The best crop I know for building the fertility of a very poor field before sowing it down to a ley is sweet clover. I have written in another part of this book about the value of this legume in gathering nitrogen and contributing organic matter to the soil; the way I use it in reclaiming a poor field ready for a herbal pasture is as follows.

Sow the field with 20 lb. an acre of sweet clover alone, or with H.1 short-rotation ryegrass at 18 lb. and sweet clover at 14 lb. an acre. The inclusion of ryegrass means that it can be grazed in an emergency, and sweet clover alone is not suitable for more than very limited grazing. The addition of ryegrass slightly reduces its value as a purely soil-improving crop, but it does give one the alternative of grazing.

But my main object in using sweet clover in this way is to feed it back to the soil, and for this purpose alone the sweet clover is better on its own.

The process of feeding the clover to the soil is, then, to mow it (with the swathe board taken off the mower) just before it comes to flower, and let it lie on the soil as a mulch. Allow it to grow nine inches to a foot high again, and mow in the same way, once more leaving the crop on the ground. Repeat this process as often as the crop grows up nine to twelve inches, until it is decided to prepare for sowing the ley.

Then the last growth of sweet clover is disced or rotavated into the soil thoroughly enough to leave a seed bed fine enough for the small seeds of the ley. Then the herbal ley is sown (not later than early September) on the disced-in sweet clover. Spring-sown sweet clover will provide two mulches in the year of sowing, and two further mulches in the following spring, and summer before discing in the third crop of its second year in late July ready for sowing the new pasture in August. If Short-Rotation ryegrass is sown with it, you can, at a pinch (though it delays the build-up of fertility for the soil), take a cut for silage if you are short of other greenstuff.

The above sweet clover fertility-building mulch is made doubly valuable if a dressing of organic manure can be applied before sowing the sweet clover, or at the time of discing in the last growth of sweet clover: for this multiplies greatly the bacteria which utilize the disced-in sweet clover.

It is usually considered essential to inoculate (i.e. dress with a bacterial culture) sweet clover or lucerne before sowing on land which has not grown either of these crops in the few years preceding sowing. I have found that where the organic content of the soil is high, this is quite unnecessary. If there is any doubt about the adequacy of the organic content of the soil, it would be wiser to use the culture obtainable from the seeds-man. But avoid this trouble in the future by building up the organic matter in the soil.

CHAPTER XII

The Struggle to Maintain Crop Yields Against the Defertilizing Effects of Chemical Soil Stimulants

Having demonstrated the establishment and maintenance of productive pastures by organic methods which are available on the farm for every farmer, I want to examine the orthodox efforts to maintain the crop yields upon which our soil chemists and plant breeders have been engaged in the past fifty years.

If you ask any orthodox agronomist what has been the trend of crop yields in the past fifty years, without any reference to statistics he will tell you, without hesitation, that yields have been going up and up. If he is a plant breeder or botanist he knows that tremendous advances have been made in the breeding and selection of heavy yielding varieties and strains. He knows the immense superiority of modern cereal, grass and clover seeds, compared with the unselected strains of our grandfathers.

If he is a soil chemist he believes that the genius of his chemical peers has taught us how to supply in exact proportions all the elements required to gain maximum yields from the heavy-yielding modern crop varieties. We have learned to correct all soil deficiencies and to take advantage of weather conditions by applying chemical stimulants at the right time. We have learned to control crop diseases and pests; and with modern machinery we can do the work so much quicker, making us less subject to climatic vagaries.

In other words, without need to make a check on statistics it should be safe to assume that there have been colossal increases in the productivity of all our crops—according to the orthodox expert of to-day.

20. All her life on mother's milk, silage and grazing only. Now, calving in with her second calf Polden Golden Sunset is yielding 48 lb. daily yield with 1 lb. per gallon of dredge corn supplemented by a Natural Mineral Mixture (powerful seaweed and herbs) in additional to 'fertility pastures.'

21. Three matrons in the Polden herd: Haughty Hetty, Springtime and Dolly Daydream, who have lived all their lives on herbal leys and silage made from these leys. Note the capacious bellies.

22. Polden Haughty Hetty in mid-winter at the peak of a 1,300 gallon 5.76% lactation on self-service silage and kale—at 11 years old.

23. Polden Haughty Hetty—showing her condition in the spring following the above winter photograph; recently calved. 'Steamed up' only on fertility pastures she was giving, when this photo was taken, 72 lbs daily, twice milking, at 11 years old.

But an examination of crop records and statistics shows that such opinions are but wishful thinking. For, without the work of selecting and breeding leafy strains of grasses and clovers, and the heavy-yielding disease-resistant strains of wheat, by men tike Sir Albert Howard and Sir George Stapledon and the plant-breeding stations of the world, there would have been a serious and rapid decline in yields during the past century. If we are to accept the claims that improved varieties are so vastly superior in yield and disease-resistance, to the varieties commonly in use 50-100 years ago, it becomes evident from official statistics that the immense and increasing use of chemical fertilizers has in fact had a depressing effect on average yields of practically all crops. For all that improved varieties have been able to do, is barely to maintain the recorded yields of fifty years ago—with only infinitesimal increases, which are in any case only to be expected from improved cultivations and harvesting techniques, from a few crops.

Examine the table of officially-recorded yields on page 96. Consider the yields in recent years with the fertilizer expenditure 'needed', or at any rate used, to achieve them. We have glibly gone on accepting and believing the oft-repeated argument that science is mastering mother nature, improving on nature, and forcing the earth to yield tenfold and a hundredfold—or modestly to make two blades of grass grow where one grew before, and other such propaganda for the rape of the earth.

This book is concerned mainly with pastures. How does the chemist explain his failure to maintain the yields of ley pastures compared with the average of the years 1903-12? In the years 1903-12 little, if any chemical fertilizers were used on grassland. To achieve an average yield of just about the same as our grandfathers did, we spent in Britain an average of £10 million a year on chemically dressing our pastures (i.e. one-sixth of the annual expenditure of £61 million from figures on June 4th return, 1953, which showed one-sixth of total crops down to temporary pastures). The average yield of leys in 1903-12 was 29.5 cwt. an acre—with virtually no fertilizers; the average yield in the years 1939-53, when the science of ley farming and government pressure for the development of ley farming was at its highest peak, the average yield was only 29.41 cwt. an acre.

ESTIMATED YIELDS PER ACRE OF THE PRINCIPAL CROPS

Crop	Unit	Great Britain (i) 10-year average 1903-12	United Kingdom (ii) 10-year average 1909-48	United Kingdom					
				1949 (iii)	1950 (iii)	1951 (iii)	1952 (iii)	1953 (iv)	average 1939-53
Wheat	cwt.	17.7	18.9	22.5	21.0	21.7	22.7	24.0	21.64
Barley	cwt.	16.6	17.7	20.7	19.2	20.3	20.5	22.7	19.19
Oats	cwt.	15.4	16.7	18.4	17.3	18.3	19.2	19.8	17.65
Potatoes	tons	6.1	7.0	6.9	7.7	7.9	7.9	8.4	7.38
Turnips } Swedes	tons	14.1	14.5	14.3	15.4	16.7	16.4	18.3	15.35
Mangolds	tons	19.4	19.4	19.5	23.7	23.2	21.5	25.6	21.05
Seeds Hay (Temporary Leys)	cwt.	29.5	28.3	29.9	28.8	30.5	31.5	31.9	29.41
Pasture Hay (Permanent pastures)	cwt.	23.7	20.8	21.2	21.2	22.0	22.8	23.5	21.47

(i) Calculated from *Annual Abstract of Statistics* No. 65, H.M.S.O.
(ii) Agricultural Statistics, 1949-50 (1952). H.M.S.O.
(iii) Annual Abstract of Statistics No. 90, H.M.S.O.
(iv) Calculated from *Monthly Digest of Statistics,* No. 98, H.M.S.O.

ESTIMATED EXPENDITURE ON ARTIFICIAL FERTILIZERS IN THE UNITED KINGDOM

Fertilizer years (July 1st-June 30th)

	1949-50	1950-51	1950-52	1952-53	1953-54
A. *Straight fertilizers:*	£	£	£	£	£
Sulphate of ammonia	2,070,800	2,558,500	2,603,500	2,986,900	2,755,800
Other nitrogenous	2,995,300	3,867,700	4,672,200	6,090,300	6,707,400
Superphosphate	2,489,600	2,075,500	2,810,500	5,065,200	4,537,000
Ground rock Phosphate	597,200	701,500	623,500	1,042,500	852,100
Basic slag	2,687,100	4,176,000	3,370,000	5,005,800	4,412,600
Other Phosphates	171,700	330,800	771,500	1,918,500	2,524,500
Potash	1,092,000	962,800	907,900	1,169,500	917,700
B. *Compound fertilizers*	24,035,600	31,570,100	30,207,500	38,047,800	38,328,000
Total	36,139,300	46,242,900	45,966,600	62,145,500	61,035,100

Notes.—(1) Expenditure has been calculated from returns of total fertilizer deliveries by manufactures and importers, collected by the Ministry of Agriculture.

(2) For 1949-50 and 1950-51, the subsidized (net) expenditure is shown, but for the remaining years no account is taken of subsidy refunds paid to farmers.

ESTIMATED EXPENDITURE ON ARTIFICIAL FERTILIZERS IN THE UNITED KINGDOM

(Adjusted for inflation, 2006*)

	1949-50	1950-51	1950-52	1952-53	1953-54
	£	£	£	£	£
A. Straight fertilizers:					
Sulphate of ammonia	49,025,411	55,511,748	51,732,465	57,555,651	52,165,690
Other nitrogenous	70,912,617	83,917,446	92,838,265	117,356,182	126,967,175
Superphosphate	58,940,357	45,032,102	55,845,628	97,603,161	85,882,767
Ground rock Phosphate	14,138,489	15,220,438	12,389,165	2,088,308	16,129,757
Basic slag	63,616,096	90,606,628	66,963,091	99,467,015	83,527,947
Other phosphates	4,064,934	7,177,364	15,329,978	36,968,267	47,784,314
Potash	25,852,695	20,889,861	18,040,294	22,535,516	17,371,526
B. Compound fertilizers	569,033,918	684,976,128	600,233,700	7,331,566,745	725,526,712
Total	855,584,528	1,003,331,716	913,372,587	1,197,503,94	1,112,349,988

*Editor's note: The author's historic financial data was converted to modern currencies and approximately adjusted for inflation, using the consumer price index. This most certainly will not correlate to modern costs and prices, but should be utilized for general directional trends only.

ESTIMATED EXPENDITURE ON ARTIFICIAL FERTILIZERS IN THE UNITED KINGDOM

(Adjusted for inflation, 2006*)

	1949-50 $	1950-51 $	1950-52 $	1952-53 $	1953-54 $
A. Straight fertilizers:					
Sulphate of ammonia	90,206,757	102,141,616	95,187,736	105,902,397	95,984,870
Other nitrogenous	130,479,215	154,408,101	170,822,408	215,935,374	233,619,601
Superphosphate	108,450,257	82,859,067	102,755,956	179,589,816	158,024,291
Ground rock Phosphate	26,014,819	28,005,606	22,796,064	3,842,486	29,678,752
Basic slag	117,053,617	166,716,196	123,212,087	183,019,308	153,691,423
Other Phosphates	7,479,478	13,206,350	28,207,159	68,021,611	87,923,138
Potash	47,568,959	38,437,345	33,194,141	41,465,350	31,963,609
B. Compound fertilizers	1,047,022,409	1260,356,076	1,104,430,009	13,490,082,811	1,334,969,150
Total	1,574,275,531	1,846,130,357	1,680,605,559	2,203,407,258	2,125,860,352

*Editor's note: The author's historic financial data was converted to modern currencies and approximately adjusted for inflation, using the consumer price index. This most certainly will not correlate to modern costs and prices, but should be utilized for general directional trends only.

The fall in permanent pasture yield of 1949-53, alongside the minute rise in temporary ley yield during the same period, assuming that both receive fertilizers (which is a reasonable assumption) would seem to indicate that in spite of—or perhaps you may well say *because* of chemical stimulus—the permanent pasture yields have fallen—whereas the temporary ley, by virtue of its improved strains of leafy grass and clover, has gained in the years 1949-53 a slight increase, in *spite* of chemical manures and poison sprays.

Total Fertilizer Consumption in tons 1949-53

U.K. Fertilizer consumption year ended 30th June 1953 in thousand tons	Nitrogen (N)	Phosphoric Acid (P₂O₅)	Potash K₂O	Total consumption in thousand tons
1949	185	419	196	800
1950	213	461	234	908
1951	211	427	226	864
1952	182	275	170	627
1953	210	400	211	821

Monthly Digest of Statistics No, 94, October 1953, H.M.S.O.

The latest figure for 1953 shows a consumption of 800 thousand tons, costing the farmer £61,000,000 a year. Amounts spent on various chemical fertilizers in each of the years 1949-54 are shown in the official table on page 99. As a statement of the immense cost to British agriculture, considered by the orthodox authorities to be essential for the maintenance of the yields set out in the table on page 98, it makes interesting reading; especially when considered against my demonstration that every penny of it can be saved by the methods advocated in my books.

The sceptic, especially one with an interest in selling chemicals or a prejudice in their favour, will point out that the reason why average yields have so little increased is that farmers still do not use *enough* fertilizers; that though some are securing more than these average yields (I have no difficulty, on *poor* land, in beating *all* those figures with no fertilizers at all), others mask the increase by gaining less than they would if they spent more.

This merely shows that some yields must be greatly below those of the good farmers of the years 1903 to 1912, to pull down yields of two to even three and a half tons of wheat to the low average of only 24 cwt. an acre in 1953, and to remove the credit which is due to the skill of the plant breeder; the quality of the land and its distribution would of course remain unchanged in these comparisons throughout the years covered. We may, of course, now be growing more wheat on poor land; but it is amazing to find that our yields of seeds-hay have increased so very little since 1912, and, taking the average for the years 1939-53, they have actually fallen, with all the work of Sir George Stapledon and Aberystwyth added. It is even more remarkable that in 1950, when farmers used the greatest amount of nitrogenous fertilizers in history, they produced less good hay than in 1952, when we used roughly 180,000 *fewer* tons of these fertilizers. For weather conditions showed no appreciable influence on the yields of either of these two years.

The fact is, that figures of fertilizer consumption measure not the increasing fertility of our land (those who take over a farm will know how short a time established farming custom expects fertilizers to stay in the land) but the size of the dose the soil is expected to swallow, and the bill agriculture has to pay. The return in yields, apart from any consideration of quality, is a very poor average increase for the immense amount of money spent by farmers who can ill afford it, and who, if they did more careful costings, would realize what little return they get from wasting their money in this way.

We can begin to call ourselves farmers when we learn to practice *husbandry* instead of *banditry;* when we learn to utilize the free fertility laid at our feet by a benevolent providence, instead of deliberately destroying our resources and relying on the manufacturing chemist to save us. All *he* can do in the long run, for that is the sole reason for the existence of any commercial undertaking of the financial magnitude of most chemical combines, is to pay dividends to the shareholders (in which your government has some financial interest too, by way of income tax and profits' tax). And those dividends and taxes come out of *your* future soil fertility. When that is ruined and you are bankrupt, some other fool will come along and buy the latest chemical to 'restore' the soil structure that the same manufacturers' chemical fertilizer or poison spray has destroyed.

Already we have seen the first of these 'soil conditioners' openly admitted by its inventor to be designed to correct the damage caused by the excessive use of his own firm's chemical fertilizers!

And it will still be easier for governments to collect income tax from directors' salaries, from shareholders' interest taxed at source, and profits' tax on the millions of profits made by the chemical combines, than from the farmer's precarious bank overdraft (even *that* only granted to an infinitesimal proportion of the value of the farmer's few cows and pigs).

This book is not the place to argue the case against government policy or chemical combines. But it is interesting to compare the balance sheet of the farming community with that of the chemical industry, and then ask why it should be necessary for the taxpayer to subsidize the price of chemical fertilizers. It can hardly be claimed that the price of chemicals cannot be reduced while such vast profits are made on their sale to the farmer.

The process whereby chemical combines are able to use governments as their chief salesmen is ever a mystery to the farmer, who is immediately condemned as inefficient if he is unable to sell his produce below cost of production.

It is extremely difficult for the taxpayer to obtain the facts on agricultural subsidies, or to think straight about them; but it is clear that the subsidy on fertilizers is not paid to farmers but to chemical manufacturers.

To the farmer, who is being ever more tightly squeezed between falling produce-prices and rising wages and other costs, the solution is now simple; he can learn to do without this expensive and fortunately unnecessary item of his budget by adapting his farming to make use, instead, of the free processes of nature, which have hitherto largely been neglected, but which this book seeks to describe in a practical way.

CHAPTER XIII

Cost of Making & Returns from Grazing the Ley

There are still farmers who question the wisdom of breaking old pasture and replacing it, either after corn crops or direct, with a new seeds' mixture. There are many more who, in accepting the necessity for renewing their pastures periodically, buy their seeds' mixtures on price rather than a careful study of ingredients, the individual functions of each ingredient and their potential productivity.

The following costings for a complex, and at first sight apparently extravagant mixture, as well as a comparatively simple mixture—each on similar soil—give a convincing answer to both the sceptic and the scrooge. The figures show how profitable re-seeding with even a simple mixture can be; but they demonstrate even more convincingly the vastly greater production that is possible from a carefully chosen complex herbal mixture. And what these figures have not assessed is the benefit in animal health which resulted from the herbal pasture as compared with the shallow-rooting simple mixture. But that, considerable as it is, was not the intention of this chapter, which is to say that no land, however rough or poor, will not pay to re-seed, if the methods for building fertility pastures are followed.

COSTS AND RETURNS ON TWENTY ACRES HERBAL LEY

(Two fields of twelve and eight acres)
Direct seeded after green-manuring crop.
Mixture

8 lb. Perennial Ryegrass, S.23 and S.24
10 lb. Cocksfoot, S.143 and S.26   } equal quantities of each strain
8 lb. Timothy, S.51 and S. 48

1 lb. Rough Stalked Meadow Grass
1 lb. Meadow Fescue
3 lb. Late-flowering Red Clover
1 lb. S.100 White Clover
1 lb. Wild White Clover
2 lb. Chicory
4 lb. Burnet
2 lb. Sheep's Parsley
2 lb. American Sweet Clover
2 lb. Lucerne
1 lb. Kidney Vetch
1 lb. Plantain
6 lb. Italian Ryegrass

———

53 lb. an acre, costing £10 an acre.

———

Costs

	£	2006* £	$
Seed at £10 (£237*)	200	4,735	8,712
Composting	50	1,184	2,178
Mustard	20	473	871
Discing in Green Crop	30	710	1,307
Rolling	10	237	436
Sowing Seed	5	118	218
Rolling	10	237	436
	£325	7,694	14,157

Editor's note: The author's historic financial data was converted to modern currencies and approximately adjusted for inflation, using the consumer price index. This most certainly will not correlate to modern costs and prices, but should be utilized for general directional trends only.

or 20 acres at say £16.5s. an acre—an extremely expensive ley by ortho-dox standards. But I have deliberately chosen this extravagant example to demonstrate manuring, the importance of not stinting seeds, cultivations, and organic or green in establishing the best leys, and to show how hand-somely it has paid in spite of (perhaps because of) the initial cost.

The ley was not costed in its first three years but even in its fourth year it produced from April 1st to October 31st, £1,484 worth of milk.

The only assistance given was the use of one ton of dredge corn valued at £30, i.e. net production of milk from the ley alone was £1,254 or a total output of £74an acre in the summer months only of its fourth year. Though actual figures are not available it is reasonable to assume that its produc-tion was at least equal in each of the previous three summers.

The only treatment the fields had during their four years of life were one light dressing of compost, not more than five tons an acre, and frequent topping with the mower, occasionally feeding back rather a heavier growth than is customary, with the normal topping off after grazing.

Grazing was closely controlled by means of an electric fence limiting the cows to not less than ten cows to the acre—moving them when growth was not quite all grazed, mowing off the residue and leaving it as a mulch to feed back to the soil, and moving the cows to the next paddock whether or not there was much growth on the new paddock. Except for a short spell of a few weeks' drought in midsummer, there was usually more than enough growth on the new paddock before the cows were ready for it, for the twenty acres was divided into nine change paddocks. Indeed at two periods of the year it was possible to cut from growth surplus to the cows' grazing requirements a total of eight tons of tripod hay and twenty tons of silage.

This compares with the much lower costs *and* returns on a proportion-ately lower acreage of a simple mixture as follows:

> 10 lb. Perennial Ryegrass
> 10 lb. Cocksfoot
> 2 lb. S.100 Clover
> 3 lb. Late-flowering Red Clover
> ———
> 25 lb. an acre, costing 85s. an acre for twelve acres
> ———

Costs

	£	s.	d.	2006* £	$
Manure	26	0	0	616	1,133
Sowing	1	12	0	38	70
Rolling	6	0	0	142	261
Seed	51	0	0	1,207	2,222
Rolling	6	0	0	142	261
Fencing	4	0	0	95	174
	£94	12	0	2,240	4,121

or £7 15s. an acre, or roughly half the cost of the good herbal ley done well with green-manuring crop.

This mixture provided a good long grazing period, the perennial rye-grass predominating in April and May with an abundance of S.100 clover; the cocksfoot providing most of the bulk with late-flowering red clover in June and July and both coming well again in late August to October. This field was also divided with an electric fence and grazed at the rate of ten cows to the acre rotationally.

Returns

	£	2006* £	$
Milk	715	16,927	31,146
Less additional foodstuffs	91	2,154	3,964
	£624	14,773	27,182

Editor's note: The author's historic financial data was converted to modern currencies and approximately adjusted for inflation, using the consumer price index. This most certainly will not correlate to modern costs and prices, but should be utilized for general directional trends only.

or approximately £52 an acre in its first year or £22 an acre less than the herbal ley in its fourth year.

There are very few areas of land, however rough, so long as a tractor is capable of being negotiated around them, that will not pay handsomely for re-seeding with a good mixture. I have described some of my hill re-seeding experiences in earlier writings, but it is worth repeating one of them here from *Fertility Farming*.

When I first started to clear the scrub on Ball Hill, ready to re-seed it, the local pundits were extremely sceptical, though, I fancy a little curious. It had never been more than a rabbit-run before, and even the rabbits had to move down the hill to find food. The soil is shallow and the slope is such that a crawler tractor could only plough it one way, and that with some trepidation on the part of the driver.

My neighbour said: 'It's all very nice as a piece of spectacular work, but it won't pay you.' I did not think I should lose anything on it and, in any case, I could not make the hill any worse than it was. I had been costing my leys lower down the hill and knew that if I could get a 'take' I should not be out of pocket.

The County Agricultural Committee was at that time quoting £10 an acre for average re-seeding work, and in the minds of many farmers even this price seemed too high when set against estimated returns. I could not get a quotation for Ball Hill, which meant that the cost was likely to be in excess of a price which was considered by many to be prohibitive.

Neither the County Agricultural Committee nor the various other advocates of ley farming have yet been able to provide figures, derived from farm costings, to show convincingly that the re-seeding of some of our *best* pastures is a profitable proposition. The best that has been offered in the way of encouragement is the vague promise of two or three times the grazing capacity, depending on the quality of the land re-seeded.

But the man who considers his present pastures good is not going to rip up his good old grass, spend £10 to £15 an acre on re-seeding it, and run the risk of an unsuccessful take, merely on the strength of an uncertain prospect of doubled grazing capacity. He will prefer the certain grazing for half the stock, and resort to the nitrogen bag for a temporary increase in stocking capacity—unless he is convinced in actual demonstration, backed by evidence of solid returns under ordinary farming conditions.

Failing authentic details of this kind I tried to produce them for myself, and found that the claims made for leys, which have been guesses in most cases, are extremely modest when compared with the costed returns from well-managed leys.

The Dairy Farmer is now sponsoring a most valuable grassland recording scheme, which will do more than all past expert advocacy to demonstrate the value of the ley and to improve grassland utilization.

It is to be hoped that growers of the herbal leys described in this book will take part and show the superior yields of these herbal leys or fertility pastures.

Ball Hill cost me over £12 an acre; I had no cash crop to take in the first year; yet it paid the full cost and a profit in grazing value in twelve months from the time of seeding. And this was from store cattle only: the returns from milking cows would no doubt have been much more.

The six acres provided me with 304 heifer-weeks of grazing during the first twelve months from seeding. At a charge of 5s. per head per week, which is reasonable considering the high quality of the grazing and the grand condition in which the heifers were maintained, the repayment on my outlay of £74 17s. 11d. was £76.

This return was purely from heifer and in-calf cow grazing. No account was taken of milk returns on two occasions when the cows were turned in to help control the growth. This means, then, that my ley was paid for in its first year, leaving me with grazing of a quality equal to the best in the district, in place of a useless scrubby sheep-run that would not support a buck rabbit before. The re-seeding was done in 1943, and was repeated in 1951, so that the initial cost was spread over eight years.

It is clear beyond doubt from these figures that good leys pay well, both as grazing for young stock and for milking cows. While the visible profit is the greater when milk cows are the agents of conversion, the foundation of sound health which young stock undoubtedly gain from ley grazing probably raises the lower cash returns of this class of grazing to a level of equal value with dairy-cow leys.

But if, by cheap mixtures and stinted cultivations, the attempt is made to keep down costs, ley farming will soon land the most affluent farmer in queer street. The best obtainable mixture for the class of land, carefully sown in well-cultivated land which has previously been well supplied with organic manure and green manuring crops, followed by intelligent management, will more than repay the original cost of a four-year ley *every* year of its life.

The mixture I used for Ball Hill was similar to that on page 103.

I have since found, for very shallow hill land liable to suffer from lack of moisture, the following mainly tap-rooted herb mixture will survive the worst droughts—by penetrating the rock for its last drop of moisture:

>4 lb. Crested Dogtail
>4 lb. Tall Fescue
>4 lb. Lucerne
>4 lb. Ribgrass or Common Plantain (Plantago lanceolata)
>2 lb. Late-flowering Red Clover
>2 lb. Alsike
>2 lb. Trefoil
>1 lb. S.100 White Clover
>2 lb. American Sweet Clover
>1/2 lb. Yarrow.
>1 lb. Broad Leaved Plantain (Plantago Major)

Ball Hill provided in subsequent years an average of £40 an acre of grazing for four years, and rapidly deteriorated in the fifth to the seventh years because of the thin soil and its exposure to the sun as it faced due south.

It was duly re-seeded in the eighth year with a deep-rooting herbal mixture at an increased cost, and should now last longer and produce even more heavily for the initial period of stocking it has had; though as it has been turned over to pigs, they may by their damage shorten the life of the ley. They have a great fondness for the roots of the deep-rooting herbs when they are folded at all thickly on the ground—and this is likely to happen. However, though experts were discouraging I am convinced that bringing six acres of one-in-four slope into production, first to graze heifers and now to graze the pigs of my successor, was well worth while and a great justification of the ley as a food-producer and soil-saver.

The man who is aiming at 800 to 900 gallons a lactation on cheap but healthy food, with the profit high because his labour cost is low and his fertilizer and cake bill non-existent, gets even greater advantages from re-seeding with herbal leys.

These advantages are not easy to measure, but, put in motoring terms, one of them is the longer life of the 'engine', in this case the cow, from not running it 'flat out'. Consider these replacement costs: if you rear a Jersey calf on a cow it will cost not more than £10 to do it well without getting it too fat; see my book, *Herdsmanship*, for my rearing methods. It is weaned from milk on to roughage—grass in summer, silage and perhaps sometimes a little hay in winter, and has nothing else—and *needs* nothing else but its natural food after all—until it calves into the herd. The cost of grass and silage is not more than 2/6 £10 a week for say twenty months after weaning, say £10. The calf has helped itself to milk from a cow, it helps itself to grass from the ley and silage from the silage heap, so labour costs chargeable to it are small: £5 for labour under this system is a generous charge—making the total cost of bringing the heifer into the herd £25.

If you want to buy a replacement for the cow you've ruined by 'reckless driving' you will pay 80-100 guineas for a moderate specimen. If you have more money than sense you will pay 200 or 300 guineas for the daughter of a cow that has been raced full out to 1,500 or 2,000 gallons of milk, leaving her no reserves of health to transmit to her progeny.

So rear your own my lazy way, on mother's milk and grass or silage from healthy leys; drive her within the 'speed' limit of her breeding, and spread your already low outlay over an extra four or five lactations, as you can easily do with grass-fed cows. Spend your money on good organic herbal leys, and you won't have to spend your money on useless, and in many cases harmful, veterinary drugs.

CHAPTER XIV

Consult the Cow

The leys I was reared on were of two types, one of three years' duration for grazing in the first year, hay and grazing in the second year and grazing in the third year; the other a two-year ley which was used mainly for haymaking, being mown in both years of its life with the after-grass of the second year being ploughed in as a green manure. But in both these cases the mixtures were of a few ingredients designed primarily for bulk yield, with little regard for their effect on the soil, and no expectation of deriving any benefit for the grazing animal, or for the top soil from the subsoil, by means of deep-rooting ingredients in the ley. Three or four grasses and two clovers were about the limit of our imagination, or should I say rather the imagination of the seedsmen and agricultural advisers of the day, in making up the mixture.

In spite of the experiences of men like R. H. Elliot, the trend of scientific development in ley farming has been to simplify even these simple mixtures which were commonly used in north-country ley farming; and until recently there has been great hope for mixtures containing as little in variety as one or two grasses and one or two clovers, making up the deficiencies of such a mixture and the difficulties of getting a complete and quick coverage of the soil in establishing the ley, by heavy dressings of artificial fertilizers at the time of seeding. Where the sole consideration in ley farming is to obtain the maximum yield of hay, silage or grazing, with possibly some minor and quite secondary benefit from ploughed-in after-grass and nitrogen fixation by the clover, there might be some argument on purely commercial grounds for such a simple mixture; but one only has to give a little thought to the needs and preferences of the grazing animal to realize that the simple mixture is far from ideal in many respects. We have all by this time had the experience of seeing grazing cattle leave a lush ley of simple mixture to graze in preference an old pasture with little apparent growth but containing a wider variety of ingredients than even Elliott attempted. Attracted by the low cost of the simple mixture and the strong scientific advocacy by agricultural 'experts', I started my own ley farming with these simple mixtures; and I certainly had many experiences, which were discouraging to say the least, of seeing my herd on admittance in the early spring to a fresh, lush ley, instead of putting their heads down and grazing undiscriminatingly through the middle of the ley, walking out to the hedgerow and grazing round it or even over the hedge if they could get there, in preference to the simple mixtures I had sown.

This sort of experience quickly taught me to consult the cow at every opportunity when I was considering ways of feeding her, and especially where matters of economy and profits were concerned: for, unlike humans whose palates are so perverted that they cannot be relied upon to decide by taste what is good for them—in fact what we like most so often is bad for us—a cow, I believe, is still the best judge of the right diet, at least as far as her own health goes. And if a diet keeps her in health I have found it safe to assume that it also enables her to produce at a profit. Producing milk at a profit is so closely bound up with the whole question of maintaining the animal in health these days, that the health of the animal might well become the primary factor in deciding the manner of feeding the cow.

I must say that my cows, after their first course round the hedgerow, always without fail came back to the simple mixtures in the ley and grazed it extremely well; but the fact that they felt the necessity for an hors-d'œuvres of much wider variety than my man-made menu offered them, was a clear indication that the simple ley mixture was entirely unrealistic in its approach to cow nutrition, and it seemed reasonable that I should assume also that it was unprofitable. The fact that I was having more than my fair share of disease in the herd at that time, when the main grazing was on simple mixtures, did not seem to me to be without significance.

From that time I began to widen the range of ingredients included in my ley mixtures, until they reached the complexity of the herbal mixtures which I now consider to be an essential part of profitable and healthful animal production.

Though consulting the cow provided my first clues in developing the ley mixtures most suited to economical milk production, I have discovered since that the preference of the cow appears to coincide with the requirements of the soil, when we follow nature's method of planning the pasture primarily as a fertility-builder. The verdict of the soil in its judgment of the comparative merits of the complex herbal ley and the simple orthodox mixture was uncompromisingly shown in the yields of crops which followed the ley, though there was no doubt in my mind that I had been right to regard the herbal mixture as the best when putting the requirements of soil-fertility first. When I came to compare the yields which followed the herbal ley with those which followed the simple ley, not only in crop yields did I see this advantage, but in milk yields also. Two fields in particular provided interesting information on this point: both were on similar soils and both leys sown in these fields were of the same age: the only difference was in the ingredients of the seed mixture. The first field was a simple mixture of Cocksfoot, Perennial Rye Grass, Late-flowering Red Clover, S.100 White Clover and 1 lb. an acre of Chicory as the only tap-rooted herb, a total of 25 lb. to the acre. The second field was sown to a complex mixture of grasses, clovers and herbs including the same grasses as the first field, but in addition 3 lb. an acre of Chicory, 4 lb. of Burnet, 2 lb. of Sheep's Parsley, 2 lb. of Kidney Vetch, 1 lb. of Yarrow, 2 lb. of Lucerne and 2 lb. of American Sweet Clover: a total of 45 lb. to the acre. Both fields achieved a more or less equal establishment, and at times of grazing appeared to have a similar yield of weight, although the second field, by virtue of its herbs, appeared to be slightly more bulky.

Throughout the life of these two leys, for a period of four to five years without exception, no matter what the variation in apparent length of growth—which was deliberately varied for test purposes—whenever the cows left the first field to go to the second, the milk yield was increased. This happened at all times of the year: even when the cattle were taken from the first field while there was still ample grazing and moved to the second field, before it appeared to the human eye to have what would appear to be adequate grazing. In other words, though there was at times during the grazing of the first field a greater quantity of starch-equivalent and protein-equivalent, the recognized nutritional requirements available for each cow to graze, there were some other factors present in the grazing of the second field which influenced milk yield so much that they enabled the cows to give a greater quantity of milk on a smaller consumption of starch- and protein-equivalent; or at least on a pasture from which it appeared more difficult to obtain the same quantity of starch-and protein-equivalent during an equal period of grazing.

I don't think even the most ardent advocate of chemical analysis in relation to animal nutrition will consider me unreasonable in declaring that the factor influencing the greater milk yield from the herbal ley, compared with the simpler mixture, was associated in some way with the inclusion of a larger variety of herbal ingredients in the ley mixture. It could be the minerals and trace-elements brought from the subsoil by the tap roots of the herbal ingredients; it could be the influence of plant hormones peculiar to the herbal ingredients which have an influence on the digestive capacity of the cow; or it could be the effect of this herbal grazing on the bacterial flora of the cow's stomach which enables it to be more efficient in converting the constituents of its diet into milk. This illustration of the comparative effects of simple and herbal mixtures, though it was not easy to explain, nevertheless clearly showed the superior value of the herbal ley.

In order to arrive at really conclusive results in this comparison, I admit that it would be necessary to reverse the seedings in the two fields and to test whether or not the herbal ley sown in the first field would produce a greater milk yield than a simple ley mixture grazed in the second field. Unfortunately, before I was able to carry this experiment through to this logical conclusion I changed farms; but I have every intention of resuming the experiment to test beyond doubt whether or not the only factor in these differing effects on milk yield *is* the inclusion of a wide variety of herbs. In the meantime I am satisfied about the superiority of the complex herbal mixture in maintaining animal health.

Most seed mixtures are made up purely on their productive ability, with no reference to the preference of the cow. There is no record of any order of preferences of grasses over clovers or herbs over both or one another. It is strange that in all the years that farmers have been sowing ley mixtures recommended by by the college and research station experts they have never questioned the research upon which these mixtures are based.

No doubt comparisons have been made between one mixture and another in yield of grass, hay, or silage and in their ultimate effect on the yield of the cow, though even this kind of information is sadly sparse.

But in 1952 I laid down thirty-five individual plots each sown with a single ingredient of the herbal ley, using $\frac{1}{2}$ lb. of seed of each of the herbs, clovers, and the main strains of each of the grasses.

The following is a list of the individual plots:

Chicory	Smooth Stalked Meadow Grass
Yarrow	
Burnet	American Sweet Clover
Sheep's Parsley	Cocksfoot, S.26
Kidney Vetch	Cocksfoot, S.143
Ribgrass or Long-leaved Plantain	Cocksfoot Akaroa
(*Plantago Lanceolata*)	Timothy, S.50
Sainfoin	Timothy, S.51
Crimson Clover	Timothy, S.48
Broad Red Clover	Perennial Ryegrass, S.23
Alsike	Perennial Ryegrass, S.24
Italian Branching Clover	Perennial Ryegrass, S.101
Ladino Clover	H.1 Strain New Zealand Short Rotation Ryegrass
S.100 White Clover	
Late-flowering Red Clover	Italian Ryegrass
Du Puits Lucerne (Alfalfa)	Westerwolth's Ryegrass
Isle de France Lucerne (Alfalfa)	Meadow Fescue
Provence Lucerne (Alfalfa)	Tall Fescue
Rough Stalked Meadow Grass	Hard Fescue

The above are being duplicated on my present farm with the addition of

Broad Leaved Plantain *(Plantago Major)*	Fennel
	Subterranean Clover
Caraway	Rhizoma (Alfalfa)
Dandelion	Dill

The plots in my original experiment were divided from one another with strips of Chicory, which clearly distinguished each plot from the next.

The object of the plots was to observe first of all growing habits and suitability for the soil conditions on my farm; to observe which of several strains of the various grasses were best suited to my conditions; and to work out the best mixtures for varying conditions, i.e. soils, seasons and grazing at different times of the year, so that I could lay down different mixtures to provide grazing at different times of the year.

But above all I wanted to know which of these pasture ingredients my cattle liked best, and what the order of preference was for the rest. Obviously I must adjust my mixtures according to the answers my cows gave

115

to these questions. I already felt that there must be room for considerable improvement from changing some of the proportions of certain ingredients. No one I asked, of all the suppliers of ley seeds, was able to tell me what relationship the quantities of the various ingredients of the ley had to the cow's attitude to its diet.

Why, for instance, I asked, were we advised to use 8 lb. cocksfoot and only $\frac{1}{2}$ lb. yarrow? Did that mean that the cows preferred to have sixteen times as much cocksfoot as yarrow, or that sixteen times as much cocksfoot as yarrow was better for the cows' health or milk yield? The best answer I could get to that was that yarrow seed is very small and doesn't need so much to sow the same area; and that in any case it is very much dearer than cocksfoot seed. But it wasn't sixteen times as costly as cocksfoot seed—and none of those answers took any account whatever of the animal that was to graze the ley when it was established.

In fact the sum total of the reasons I was given for the proportions of ingredients included in recommended mixtures was that most mixtures were arrived at partly on a basis of price and partly by juggling with various ingredients, until what was called 'a balanced sward' was arrived at. But what is the criterion of a 'balanced sward' I was unable to discover. Except that anything known to be quite unpalatable was not included, the ultimate consumer of the ley was neither considered nor consulted by any of the pasture authorities responsible for advising on ley farming policy and technique.

And the answers I obtained from my plots soon demonstrated the wastefulness and inefficiency of planning the ley without consulting the cow.

I found, for instance, that on my soil the cows did not touch Hard Fescue. It was completely ignored by them whenever there was anything else to graze. Obviously then, this was an ingredient that I had sometimes been advised to include in ley mixtures which was an utter waste of money.

But before I go into detail about my results—a few words about the manner of arriving at them.

The plots were laid side by side consecutively alongside a roadway from which the cows could be controlled by fence—either to graze from the road without walking freely over the plots, or to be admitted free range over the plots.

The first thing I recorded in watching the establishment of the plots in the early growing stages was that four plots grew away far ahead of the rest. They were Plantain, Westerwolth's Ryegrass, Chicory and Broad Red Clover. The first deduction from that, then, was a mixture for quick estab-

116

lishment for grazing in the shortest possible time after sowing. That would be a mixture roughly as follows:

> Per acre—10 lb. Westerwolth's Ryegrass
> 3 lb. Chicory
> 3 lb. Plantain
> 3 lb. Broad Red Clover

That would, of course, not be suitable for more than a two-year ley; but it would, under good conditions, provide grazing in 6-7 weeks from the time of sowing. To give it a longer life—say 3-4 years, 6 lb. each of Perennial Ryegrass and Cocksfoot (light land) or Timothy (heavy land) and 1 lb. S.100 White Clover would need to be added.

Burnet and Kidney Vetch were both very slow to establish, partly because of dry conditions at the time—though I find Burnet is normally rather slow.

After these early and late starters the other plots followed in between fairly evenly, with the Short Rotation Ryegrass catching up the Westerwolth's long before maturity was reached. Of these two ryegrasses it is clear that though Westerwolth's might be cut ten days sooner for hay or silage than the New Zealand Short Rotation Ryegrass, the extra leafiness of the latter makes it preferable as a producer of maximum nutriment in the ley designed for quick-bulk production of high-protein fodder—either for hay or silage. It was also, of the ryegrasses, preferred to either Westerwolth's or Italian Ryegrass when the cows had free choice of grazing.

The first grazing tests took the form of a sampling session. The cows were allowed to walk alongside the plots and help themselves under the fence, in the manner which cows love, of trying the grass through the fence. We all know the habit which cows have of preferring the grass in the next field or paddock if they can get to it—and how, even with strip grazing with an electric fence, they always graze harder just under the fence into the next plot than the plot they are on. This fondness for the next paddock was extended to a choice of thirty-five next paddocks; for they were allowed to sample freely of the edge of each of the thirty-five plots daily for two weeks.

And of the thirty-five plots three were persistently eaten down while the rest were merely nibbled at; the herd would queue up to get to these three plots and each get as much as they could before they were moved on. The plots preferred were Sheep's Parsley, Plantain and Chicory.

Until the cows were later turned right on to the plots, little attention was given through the fence to any of the grasses. The ryegrasses, meadow grasses and Hard Fescue were almost untouched—Meadow Fescue and Tall Fescue were sampled.

Timothy and Cocksfoot were grazed lightly, as were all the Clovers equally. The Lucernes were untouched, as was the American Sweet Clover. Following closely behind the three favourites, in this order were Burnet, Kidney Vetch, Sainfoin and Alsike. (The Italian Branching Clover from seed directly imported failed, but I have since obtained more seed from Italian friends and found it to be palatable and productive though rather shy of a hard winter.)

Later, when all plots were well established, the cows were turned in over all the plots at once. Their preferences continued the same: Sheep's Parsley was grazed down hard before any of the others, and Plantain and Chicory were not more than a day behind. The fact that Plantain and Chicory had a much heavier crop, both thicker and longer growth (for they had established much more completely), probably puts them at least level with Sheeps' Parsley for preference. The plots were not large enough to allow all the herd to go to the plot of their choice together at the same time. So first grazing was divided between three parties of the leading cows on the Sheep's Parsley, Chicory and Plantain plots with the rest of the herd on the Burnet, Kidney Vetch and Sainfoin, waiting their turn for their favourite herbs.

Of the grasses, H.1 Short Rotation Ryegrass and Meadow Fescue were preferred to the rest; and apart from Hard Fescue, which was not liked at all, the other grasses were about equally liked as far as we could see.

The second grazing was taken by in-calf heifers and a bull. Though they followed roughly the preferences of the cows they were not so discriminating or persistent in their demand for the deeper-rooting herbs; probably because the mineral requirements were not so pressing as with the milking cows.

The bull was the only animal who appeared to enjoy the Lucernes and American Sweet Clover as well as the rest. Though he too concentrated on Sheep's Parsley, Plantain and Chicory more than any of the other plots, for the rest he did not seem to mind what it was. His usual grazing plan was to take one or two of the deep rooters as the real meat of the meal, and any of the rest to fill up on. And *my* conclusions in selecting ley mixtures came pretty close to the bull's summary—though obviously, as far as pocket and availability of seeds are concerned, I had to try to follow the finer discrimination of the cows.

It would be interesting to know whether soil conditions, both of top soil and subsoil, deficiencies and varying availability of the different minerals and trace elements, organic content and moisture, and even breed of cow, had any bearing on the choice of the cow. The only way that this information could be provided, and I think it is vital that it should be, would be for my experiment to be repeated on all classes of soil in different parts of the country and with different breeds of cattle.

This is a worthwhile task for the Ministry of Agriculture experimental farms—but if any concerned farmer is prepared to undertake such an experiment on his own farm I shall be delighted to do all I can to help with information, organically-grown seed (so that variability of seed in relation to palatability is eliminated) and record-keeping, if he will write to me. Fifty farmers, covering all breeds of cattle and a wide variety of soil types, could supply some most valuable information on ley farming in relation to cattle nutrition, if we could get such experiments going. Goat, pig and poultry breeders too might join in such experiments: for there is also much need for information about the ingredients of pastures specially sown for all these classes of livestock.

COMPARATIVE YIELDS OF GRASSES, CLOVERS AND HERBS USED IN THE LEY

Another guide to the comparative importance of the various ingredients of the pasture mixture is that of yield or productive ability. Just as there appears to be no published work on the choice of the animal in the compilation of a ley mixture, neither is there anything that I have been able to find to guide the farmer on the ingredients of the ley that are to produce the greatest bulk, individually. It may be that such a comparison of individual ingredients becomes useless once they are combined in a mixture; but while I had my individual plots I thought it would at least be interesting to make an estimate of the comparative yields as well as the order of preferences of the cattle.

Such a comparison cannot, as a private experiment, claim to be accurate; for it is not possible to get an exact weight and measurement of growth magnified from a small half-pound plot to terms of yield per acre. But I was able to measure at least the *main* yielders of bulk; and it is interesting to note that they did not coincide in all respects (though rather more closely than presently accepted recommended mixtures indicate) with the order of the animal's preference.

119

The greatest bulk was produced by thickly sown Chicory; for cut or graze as I would, no matter how frequently, it was impossible to leave the Chicory for more than a few days without fresh growth. It produced many more cuts or grazings than any other ingredient of the ley mixture.

Closely following Chicory in productive ability are Lucerne and American Sweet Clover, with American Sweet Clover the heavier of the two. Being far behind in palatability we cannot, nevertheless, consider American Sweet Clover for a larger proportion of the ley mixture because of its high yield. But it does, in consequence of this demonstration of high yield, and in view of its great contribution of nitrogen to the soil, rank high for me as a green-manuring crop for building-up fertility and raising the population of soil bacteria.

Sainfoin and Crimson Clover produced heavily of the first growth, but because of slower recovery did not yield so well in total throughout the year.

New Zealand Short Rotation Ryegrass came next in order of yield for the year, after leading on first growth. Being only a short-rotation and consequently short-lived ingredient it would not, of course, compare with any of the other ingredients' subsequent yields—a test which I hope to report in later editions of this book.

On annual yield the two grasses, Cocksfoot and Timothy, came next in that order.

Meadow Fescue, Perennial Ryegrass and Late-flowering Red Clover were next in order—all about equal in annual yield, with S.100 White Clover, Kidney Vetch, Plantain and Yarrow very closely following. Italian Ryegrass followed, with Sheep's Parsley and Tall Fescue next. I would normally have expected Italian Ryegrass to stand high in bulk annual yield, particularly as, alongside the

New Zealand Short Rotation H.1 Ryegrass, it was the quickest grass to grow—but I may have had a poor strain or weather conditions may not have suited it, for after its first great growth, it fell behind the others in total yield, while the New Zealand Short Rotation Ryegrass held its place well.

The Meadow Grasses, rough and smooth, were not among the really heavy yielders; and not developing to any great height, appear to be useful only as undergrowth, probably better suited to the sheep or horse pasture than for cattle-grazing.

Hard Fescue was by far the poorest yielder—but then it is never intended for its bulk.

Choosing a mixture in order of bulk yield—which appears to be the sole criterion of the modern seedsman, apart from some reference to competitive growing habits, one should have in order of preference something like this:

Chicory
Lucerne
New Zealand Short Rotation Ryegrass
Cocksfoot
Timothy
Meadow Fescue
Perennial Ryegrass
Late-flowering Red Clover
S.100 White Clover
Sheep's Parsley
Yarrow
Tall Fescue

As I haven't tried any mixtures on this basis yet (but intend to do so) I cannot suggest proportions—but this is a piece of experimental work which might well be worth the while of any farmer looking for maximum yields from his leys.

From these plots and bigger field and grazing experiments I have worked out mixtures for varying purposes and conditions which I recommend, with some comments on them, in Chapter XVIII.

CHAPTER XV

Herbs as Soil Indicators

One of the most fascinating and, I may say, remunerative ways of spending a holiday for the really keen farmer with the sense to use his powers of observation to increase the power of his pocket—is to go herb-hunting and to study the soil conditions indicated by the herbs that are found.

No soil analyst can tell an observant farmer what he wants to know about his soil as accurately as the herbs (or weeds if you still despise them) growing on it. Whenever I go to a fresh bit of country I want to know the sort of soil I'm walking on; and my most enjoyable occupation is to search upon it for unfamiliar herbs, which are quickly identified with the aid of those ever-absorbing pocket books, *Flowers of Wayside and Woodland*, published by Warne & Co., which are permanent passengers in the pocket of my car (except when an equally inquisitive son or member of my staff has borrowed them for the same purpose).

Equipped with these priceless books, and some knowledge of soil types which every farmer's son absorbs between the ages of five and fifty, nobody need wait the long years that it will take the agricultural advisory service to complete a soil analysis of each of his fields. The official soil analysis, in any case, only tells what the spot availability of nutrients was at one brief moment in the 365-day biological cycle of the soil.

The herbs that grow a whole season, or year after year, in your field tell you what the sum total of the four seasons has already produced, and might or might not be capable of reproducing with the wide range of domestic crops or animals that you consider growing there.

The soil chemist's analysis has as its objective, not a complete picture of soil conditions, but the key to the sale of chemical fertilizers. It is an antique device for convincing spoon-fed farmers that they are being efficient. But, based on the fallacy that the secret of successful crop-growing is knowing the 'right' quantities of N, P & K to sprinkle on the land, it is, for intelligent farmers, a long-outmoded form of grey magic. The grey or white powders which the soil chemist's report of his test tells you to use, have no bearing whatever on the particular soil conditions under proper methods of management; and no honest soil chemist to-day really believes that a spoonful of soil in a crucible in his laboratory is going to show the answer to the problems of crop production and animal health on the farm. It can only tell you what elements are available in that particular bit of soil at that particular moment; and a bit of soil taken from the same spot in the same field a few hours later will produce a completely different answer: for a change of atmospheric temperature may have set in motion a whole train of rapidly changing, but highly vital and interrelated processes. And we get plenty of changes of temperature in this country; so if you are going to rely on soil analysis to govern your fertilizer expenditure you are going to be in a pretty state of confusion should you try to get a guide from the soil analyst.

But a herb cannot hop in and out of your field in step with the British climate or the gall bladder of the soil analyst. So I suggest some acquaintance with the natural eternal guides to the conditions in your soil, which were put there for your information before people discovered that selling chemicals was an easier living than growing crops.

I cannot, in this one chapter, hope to do more than introduce this fascinating study of herbs and their meaning—and, I hope, set my readers on the hobby of a lifetime, most of which will be original research. For though we know a lot about the properties of herbs in the prevention and treatment of disease, and many books have been published on herbs and their identification, nothing that I know, until this short amateur effort of mine, has been published on the interpretation of herbs and wild plants in relation to their environment: herbs and their associations with companion plants, and herbs as indicators of soil conditions.

For me this interest has developed with my lifelong study of animal health and the search for nature's means of maintaining it. In order to discover the natural remedy for a modern animal ailment, I have needed many private consultations with my animals; and, in turn, with the herbs which nature has provided for their welfare—and ours. And in these consultations with the living manifestations of natural processes of healing, what a tremendous lot of information is revealed gratis that does not appear superficially to have any relevance to the immediate problem, but which has a vital part in the whole complex of animal husbandry and ultimately, in most cases, human health.

123

We all know that a soil which is deficient in calcium (or at least on analysis shows itself to be acid by the accepted pH measure) quickly acquires a covering of herbs or weeds which thrive under conditions of acidity. Some of these plants are themselves slightly acid or sour to the palate of the animal and are therefore not normally acceptable to the majority of farm animals. Sorrel, Sourdock, Silverweed and Yorkshire Fog are examples. Others, such as Burnet, gather calcium with their tap roots, and because of consequent palatability tend to be grazed out of existence. Soil conditions result in a deterioration of grazeable ingredients in the mixture; and the beneficial grazing of the animal in turn diminishes, with the result that an unpalatable sward predominates. The scavenging type of grazing animal, such as the sheep or the goat, is then the only animal able to survive on the changed ingredients of the pasture.

This is the state of affairs which exists on thousands of acres of so-called marginal land to-day. It is believed that because only grasses and herbs which are unpalatable to cattle grow on these 'marginal' areas, they cannot be made productive for cattle.

So thousands of acres of potentially fertile land are neglected as suitable only for rough sheep-grazing.

Yet much of this land which grows these acidity-indicating herbs, and shows a serious lack of calcium on analysis, is immediately overlying the chalk or limestone. Many thousands of acres of it are actually chalk downs or hills.

Only the deep taproots of perennial herbs can etch their way down into the chalk to release calcium for themselves; and in addition to growing the herbs which indicate the non-availability of calcium, nature has actually started the process of making available the necessary calcium, and in many such areas blatantly demonstrates to the observant farmer, with yet another well-known indicator of acidity, what needs to be done to put matters right.

Everyone who walks over these poor, acid fields feels the springy decaying turf underfoot. It is like walking over the deep pile of the newly carpeted foyer of a London theatre. And to the farmer of the land it is as costly in wasted acres as the carpeting of the cinema foyer is to the Odious Picture Corporation, Inc. The only difference is that the fabulous Odious *can* afford it; indeed it attracts profits for its owner. But the 'featherbedded' farmer can't, it only attracts picnickers to leave his gates open. Feather beds are a comfort under an aching back after a hard day's work, but not under foot on a large field that could be producing 500 gallons of milk to the acre.

But why has nature laid this mattress of turf over these thousands of acres? If we trace through the process of deduction started by the observation that the Yorkshire Fog, the Sorrel, the Annual Meadow Grass and the Ragwort grow on acid soils while ample chalk sits near their roots, and decide by this means that the soil needs *soluble* calcium, we may reasonably conclude that the covering of matted vegetation is the attempt by nature to create acids of vegetable decomposition for the purpose of releasing the chalk or limestone which is there but insoluble. The decay on these matted marginal acres is too slow to produce results, because of inadequate animal manure to feed the aerobic bacteria and supply them with sufficient nitrogen to activate the decomposition of the vegetation.

Organic matter and animal excretion to activate it; the ever-beneficent action of sun and rain to set the cycle of decay and growth in motion, are all that are needed to change the face of these barren downs.

As I write, I sit in a field of perhaps forty or fifty acres which is at present hardly capable of feeding the rabbits who share it with a few hungry store bullocks. The field adjoins a quiet seashore on one of the loveliest corners of the Cornish coast. Every year for the past ten years I have come here to write, while my sons play on the sands below; or to play cricket on this unproductive turf in the energetic interludes between writing, when I fancy myself emulating my fellow Yorkshireman, Freddie Trueman. Here are forty or fifty wasted acres, upon which, on occasions, I cannot even enjoy expending my cricketing energy, because of the swarms of seaweed flies which breed in the piles of seaweed accumulating on the sands a few yards below. And yet all this land needs, to make it grow a first-class pasture, to enable it to carry a cow to the acre, is about a tenth of the seaweed that is deposited alongside each autumn. It would not even be necessary to mix with it the sewage sludge that pours out into the surrounding sea from two adjoining towns: though, if such an obvious invitation, of nature were ever to be accepted by the local authorities, there is no reason why this now useless land could not carry *two* cows to the acre for the greater part of the year.

And we stand helpless in the face of approaching famine; we publish books by the dozen on the problems of a hungry world; we despair of that careless Creator who has landed us with a human population which threatens to outstrip world food resources!

But I have been led a long way from my Yorkshire Fog in following up its clues. Would that those of my fellow agriculturists, with the power and influence to carry them through, would observe the indications of the herbs which grow in the humus-hungry acres of a world which pours its

24. Ribgrass or Plantain. This plant was cut immediately after this photograph was taken—then photographed after ten days re-growth (see plate 25).

25. The same plant of Plantain as plate 24 ten days after being cut.

fertility down the drains to feed only fish and seaweed. It isn't only the city 'sharks' who swallow the farmers' profits: the drains of our cities and towns take more of them down to the mouths of real sharks in the sea around us; and when they are thrown back at us in the form of a seaweed fertilizer we go to the chemist for a poison spray to destroy the life which breeds in the seaweed—as though we are determined to dash human destiny on the rocks of industrial dividends and bury the bones in the barren sands of our own stupidity.

But while the little pink Thrift whispers its warning on the shores of national prodigality, there are other herbs which can guide you and me on our farms further inland, where we struggle for individual survival.

Burnet (*Poterium Sanguisorba*)

Its presence growing wild is an indication of acidity, though it becomes very predominant on the chalk where its deep roots can penetrate into the chalk to draw up the calcium released by rootlet acids. This ability to bring calcium to an acid top soil makes it an extremely valuable ingredient of the temporary pasture, balancing the deficiencies of the shallow-rooting clovers and grasses. It is relished by all stock and in consequence is often punished by too early grazing before it is established. It also takes better when seeded direct for it establishes better with plenty of sunlight and breathing space, being rather discouraged by a 'nurse' crop.

Medicinally it has tonic properties. The old herbalists believed it cleansed the heart and cheered the spirits.

There is every indication that it has this effect on sheep and cattle for they will graze it in preference to all other ingredients of the simple mixture, though its favour is about equal to Sheeps' Parsley, Plantain and Chicory in the herbal ley—depending to some extent on the soil type and mineral availability of the field in which it grows. I have written more about grazing preferences in Chapter XIV— *Consult the Cow.*

Fat Hen (*Chenopodium Album*)

You may know it by any of the following local names: Lambs' Quarters, Goosefoot, Muck Weed, Dung Weed. The last names give the clue to its taste in soil conditions. It grows only where the organic content of the soil is high and it comes in profusion on and around a farmyard manure or compost heap. It is often in companionship in this position with a very similar plant, Orache or Dungleweed; but Fat Hen is upright and does not have the spreading branches or wing-based leaves of Orache. If it becomes a nuisance on the farm you may take consolation from the knowledge that it means the fertility of the soil where it grows is as good as need be. The fact that it is an annual makes it easy to control, though because of its profuse seeding propensities it seems to have no survival problems, so long as its one requirement, rich fertile soil, is available.

RED SHANK (*Polygonum Persicaria*). Sometimes known as Willow Weed or Persicary.

A most profuse and persistent plant on heavier and damper soils. Its presence again indicates no serious lack of organic matter, for it will not prosper on very light, poor, dry soils. Where it is present then, it may be assumed that the soil is potentially very fertile and not lacking in any serious degree any essential elements. It will grow well on acid soils but favours neutral conditions as far as calcium availability is concerned. The fact that adequate organic matter is a condition of its existence, probably explains why even on lime-deficient soils it will thrive so long as humus is maintained. This, of course, also applies to the domestic crops which don't normally thrive with a lime deficiency, for they too will ignore the lime deficiency and grow well if the organic content is right.

Persicaria can be controlled by allowing it to grow alone or in a silage crop up to the flowering stage and cutting it for silage before it seeds. If the field is then only disced or rotavated it will not establish again until, you plough and bring up a previous year's seeding.

GROUNDSEL *(Senecio vulgaris)*

One of the most common of English weeds, known by everyone for its fluffy off-white birds' powder-puff seed head.

Medium rich soil conditions may be assumed from its presence. It does not favour very light acid soil. So, as with Persicaria and Fat Hen (though the latter indicates the highest fertility) it is safe to assume good fertility if Groundsel is a troublesome occupant of your soil.

CHICKWEED *(Stellaria media)*

Is also in the same company as Fat Hen in being a lover of rich, strong soil. It must have moisture and organic nitrogen and whilst it will grow a small-leaved spindly plant in medium soil it develops a large, bushy, succulent green water-cress-like growth in the rich soil that it favours.

Judge your soil by the size of its leaf in comparison with water-cress.

It is not suggested that chickweed should be sown in a pasture; but it comes voluntarily where the organic content of the soil is good—for the first year of the pasture. Though it does not persist usually after the first year, so long as it doesn't smother out everything else in the seeds' mixture, it is beneficial to the grazing animal.

Its special virtues are as a kidney tonic, a rich source of vitamin C and preventive of skin disorders. It also helps to keep clear and free from infection the internal mucous membranes, and the respiratory organs in particular.

It is beneficial in any kind of inflammation of these membranes, and helps to protect the animal against worms of all kinds, but especially husk worms, which live in the mucous deposits of the internal membrane of the lungs.

MARESTAIL *(Equisetum)*. Also Horsetails, Snakepipes, Catstails, Toad Pipe.

The main indication of this plant is of badly drained or poorly aerated soil. But it also favours the more fertile and heavier soils of neutral lime status. It is one of the most difficult weeds to eradicate and as it has no medicinal or nutritional value in agriculture (it is said to be capable of arresting the development of poliomyelitis in humans) it is only a persistent reminder that something must be done about drainage in the spot where it grows. It is a perennial which, once established, penetrates to a great depth in the rather airless subsoil of a heavy wet field.

The repeated use of a subsoiler offers the most economical and effective way of eliminating the weed, but once the soil aeration is improved it may be necessary to have a summer fallow finally to destroy it.

RIBGRASS OR PLANTAIN *(Plantago Lanceolata)*. Also known as Ribwort or long-leaved Plantain.

This plant is relished by all classes of livestock, standing ahead of all grasses and clovers, of roughly equal palatability with sheeps' parsley and chicory where cattle have a choice. It is one of the most mineral-rich of all herbs available for inclusion in the herbal ley and, whether or not it is indigenous or self-evident in the surrounding areas of the field, it should most certainly be included in all grazing pasture mixtures at the rate of at least 1 lb. an acre. I prefer 2 or 3 lb. for dairy herd grazing. Even where hay is to be made from the pasture it is not troublesome to dry, having a lower moisture content than clover.

In a silage mixture it adds greatly to the palatability of the finished silage.

In conditions of poor fertility it grows with a rosette of rather prostrate leaves, which are not easily grazed by cattle. Because of this habit on poorer soils it has been rather spurned as a weed, especially by the poison-spray salesmen whose products find an easy victim in the prostrate rosette of ribbed leaves. But given good fertility, a reasonable organic content in the soil, it grows erect and its long lance-shaped leaves, which widen with increasing fertility, grow up to allow the cows to wrap their relishing tongues around it to gather from its vigorous, abundant growth, vast quantities of nutritious health-promoting forage.

As a perennial it persists and increases in output under fertile conditions throughout each year of a four-year ley or permanent pasture.

WILD THYME (*Thymus serpyllum*)

Thrives on light, thin, rocky or stony soil over chalk or limestone, and creeps over large areas of hill and down. It prefers, and under such conditions grows more erect like the garden Thyme, a humus-rich patch on the stony hillside where the calcium of the chalk or limestone is in a soluble condition. I believe therefore that the presence of an erect growing Thyme indicates that some calcium is available in an area which may otherwise be 'lime deficient' though on the chalk or limestone.

A little Wild Thyme in the pasture is good for internal disinfectant purposes, has a soothing effect on a disturbed digestion, is a mild worm deterrent and has a beneficial effect on the bronchial tubes. It might have possibilities in the herbal pasture in very limited measure.

SAVORY—SUMMER OR WINTER (*Satureia Montana*)

This little plant is of the same botanical family as Wild Thyme but whereas Thyme likes a bit of humus to supply its soluble calcium, Savory grows well in exposed, extremely poor, rough and shallow soil which may be almost completely devoid of humus. There are two strains of the plant, one growing in summer and the other in winter. I have never seen Savory growing on any soil that was not seriously lacking in humus and it is never to be found on soil that has a reasonable degree of fertility. So it can be safely assumed that if Savory is growing, no domestic crop will be a proposition, until a heavy dressing of organic manure has been applied.

It has very small lilac flowers and tiny dark green spear-shaped leaves and a coarse stem, which makes it of little or no nutritional value, so the fact that it willnot survive on fertile soil is no loss. It is, however, of value in colic, either human or animal and is valued by goats as a preventive of stomach gases.

POPPY (*Papaver rhœas*)

Where the red field Poppy grows the soil is generally light and sandy, indicating lack of humus. It favours a very dry season and is never troublesome on the moister, fertile soils with sufficient humus to maintain optimum growing conditions for the competing crop.

It comes and goes—in other words a bad poppy year may be followed by several in which the poppy is not a troublesome weed. It is often seen to be a punishment for the farmer following the excessive use of nitrogenous fertilizers and this, I believe, is due to the humus-burning effect of synthetic nitrogen, which leaves a soil condition in which the poppy thrives.

If the poppy appears, then it is time to stop the nitrogen (and this may also mean *raw* farmyard dung with its excessive nitrogen, for poppy often follows the dung cart) and to apply a good dressing of really mature F.Y.M. or compost.

FIELD WOODRUSH *(Luzula Campestris)*

Rushes of all kinds are generally an indication of damp, sandy or salty conditions. But the Field Woodrush, with upright, little, smooth, round, wiry stem, topped by a dark brown, shiny-edged cluster of flowers, is a common sight on the dry, light-land pastures of low fertility in all parts of Britain. Its leaves may be mistaken for one of its coarser grass companions when the flower stem has not developed, but may be distinguished by the long white hairs on the grass-like leaf.

It has no value except as an indicator of poor, dry conditions and the need for organic manure to improve the moisture-holding ability of the soil.

STINKING MAYWEED *(Anthemis cotula)*

This daisy-flowered member of the Chamomile family may well be regarded as the 'blacksheep' of the Anthemis family. For whereas true Chamomile (*Anthemis nobilis*) has a pleasant scent, *cotula* is most objectionable when rubbed and has an irritating effect on the skin and nasal membranes of some people. As a soil indicator it favours acid, light gravelly conditions and low fertility. It is an extremely troublesome weed on the lighter or sandy soils which lack organic matter or moisture. On the heavier soils with much humus and moisture it will not long survive and even when established it persists only on the hard, dry cart track or foot path.

As an annual it can be controlled by mowing before seed sets. And because of the profusion of leaves which it produces, it makes a valuable contribution to soil fertility when used in this way, as a mulch, or worked into the top soil with discs or rotavator.

It has sedative properties when used medicinally, though the true Chamomile (*Anthemis nobilis*) is preferable for this purpose and is well known as a digestive tea.

CORN SPURREY (*Spergula arvensis*)

A sure indicator of light soils—on which it persists and multiplies rapidly by means of its annual seeding of round hard oil-bound seeds. It has no value except as an indication that the soil is too poor to grow satisfactory animal or human food and as a warning that a summer fallow is long overdue. One of its names, Beggar Weed, is derived from the poverty of the soil which it favours.

KNAPWEED OR HARDHEADS (*Centaurea nigra*)

This purple-flowered head with a bumble-bee brown basal cup (from which the purple petals spring) is one of the few indicators of phosphate deficiency. Most of the other poor-soil plants also indicate low availability of phosphates in the top soil but Knapweed, being a deeper rooter, able to tap phosphates unavailable to the other plants, only thrives where the phosphates are deep in the subsoil, though seriously lacking, almost to the point of absence, in the top soil.

The existence of Knapweed is one of the few justifications for the application of additional phosphates (in the form of ground phosphate rock) as well as organic manure and ground limestone or chalk.

BROAD-LEAVED PLANTAIN OR SNAKEWEED (*Plantago Major*)

This is a common plant on most soils, and will grow almost anywhere. Consequently its existence is of no value as a soil indicator. Its rosettes of broad, oval, longitudinally ribbed leaves are, however, of great nutritional value. The fact that it is sometimes called Way-bread or Bread-by-the-way indicates its nutritional value to the roving animal, or travelling man. It is equally useful to grazing animal or bird. Its long, narrow spike of seeds produces abundant food for birds and its leaf, which grows the year round under all conditions of climate and soil, makes it a universal provider.

Medicinally, it has mucilaginous properties, and its bruised or chopped leaves have great healing properties, as a fresh green poultice or rubbed into a nettle sting or fly bite.

Yarrow (*Achillea Millefolium*)

In its wild state this herb favours very dry conditions and this is just about the only thing it may guide you to as an indicator, for it grows on all types of soil, almost prostrate and tiny in poor acid soils but upright and resplendent with its 'Millefolium' or 'Thousand leaves' of pretty soft fern-like appearance, in fertile soils.

Its roots do not tolerate excessively moist conditions so that it does tend to die out on wet, heavy or badly drained land. So where it thrives the land may be assumed to be freely draining.

In addition to its high protein content it has valuable tonic and stimulant properties. Its juice applied to a cut or wound will stop bleeding.

Coltsfoot (*Tussilago farfara*)

A plant which favours heavy clay soils of medium fertility with poor drainage. It is sometimes even known as Clayweed in clay soil areas.

It is distinguishable from many similar yellow daisy-like flowers, by the fact that flowers appear before leaves. Its stem looks rather like asparagus until after flowering, when the leaves break out large and heart-shaped and develop a white down on the underside.

Though I have never known cattle to eat it, probably because they are not normally subject to the troubles which it cures, Coltsfoot leaves infused as a tea have a most beneficial influence on the bronchial tubes, and give great relief in chronic bronchitis.

Cleavers (*Galium aparine*)

Also known as Goosegrass, Sticky Willy, Clivers, Sweet-hearts. A plant whichis commonly found climbing among the hedgerow bushes and spreading into such fields as are fertile enough to sustain it. It favours straw crops, around which it can attach its hooked, bristly, sticky, square stems. It spreads by 'burs' or round hard bristly seed heads which attach themselves to clothes and the hair of animals.

If it is present in an arable silage crop you may well be pleased for it is an excellent blood purifier, being rich in iron, chlorophyll, some iodine and all the vitamins. Cut in the green stage it is easily controlled, for it is an annual which spreads only by seeding. It must, however, be cut before the seed is advanced enough to pass through the cattle which eat the silage. If the seed does set hard the best use for it is to feed poultry. They love the seed and readily consume the whole plant when its iron and iodine content are very valuable, especially to yarded or deep-litter birds. It is well worth while to gather Cleavers solely for the purpose of feeding it to intensively-kept poultry.

DUNGLEWEED OR ORACHE *(Atriplex patula)*

Commonly known as Dungleweed it is almost as much like another rich soil plant Dungweed (Fat Hen) as their names. But Orache has narrower snake-tongue leaves with wide-pointed winged base to the leaf. Orache is also an annual and spreads by the numerous seeds which set from its spikes of green flowers. Orache has a much more spreading, branched habit of growth than Fat Hen.

Like Fat Hen it grows on strong soils of medium high fertility, rich in organic matter. Its appearance is an indication that with proper cultivation your soil needs no manuring of any kind to enable it to grow any crop. A very cheering state for any farmer or gardener to have reached, for it is much easier to maintain such a state than to achieve it.

It is interesting to note that the natural indicators of high fertility have little or no medicinal value. Their main virtue is purely nutritional—suppliers of starch- and protein-equivalent and some vitamins—but they are normally useless as sources of mineral and trace elements.

The reason for this is that where top-soil fertility is high, the shallow-rooting plants can flourish; whereas if the top-soil is poor and incapable of supporting the shallow-rooters, only the deep-rooters can survive. And it is from the subsoil that the deep roots draw the minerals and trace-elements which have been robbed, perhaps through generations of exploitive methods—mono-cropping, mono-stocking or inadequate manuring—from the top soil.

It would be a useful piece of research work if someone, with the necessary funds to pay the very high cost of complete mineral, trace-element and vitamin analyses, would ascertain the extent to which these elements, which we know are richly present in the deep-rooting herbs, are also acquired by the shallow-rooters in a really fertile top-soil. In the meantime, a wide variety of herbage, both deep- and shallow-rooting, will ensure an adequate supply of all nutritional and health requirements, provided sufficient humus is present.

LUPINS *for phosphate-deficient soils*

As a green manure to be disced into the soil in preparation for the ley, lupins are the best crop where there is a phosphate deficiency. They appear to have a greater capacity for extracting phosphorous from the soil than any other green-manuring crop. Even from soils which, on analysis, appear to be lacking in available phosphate, lupins have the ability to make it available and to take it up. This means that when a green crop of lupins is disced or rotavated into the top-soil it adds directly a supply of phosphorous in addition to releasing more in the process of decay.

GROUND IVY (*Nepeta hederacea*)

Has a special value in kidney troubles. Because of its bitter flavour cattle will rarely eat it; but if very small quantities are growing in the ley or hedgerow the cattle will take it along with other grazing. If so taken it is beneficial to the reproductive health of both male and female animals. Its disadvantage is that it spreads rapidly over the ground, and if it is to be used is best confined to a small area rather than mixed with the other ingredients of the ley, otherwise it may not be easily controlled.

SHEPHERD'S PURSE (*Capsella bursa-pastoris*)

Because of its profuse seeding-habits, Shepherd's Purse so easily becomes a nuisance on areas of land where it is not wanted, that it is not one of the herbs I would recommend for inclusion in a herbal ley.

But it is as well to note that where it is present it may be used with benefit for feeding to cattle and goats with breeding troubles, or infused as a tea for use with dogs that have kidney trouble. It is also relished by poultry, and has a stimulating effect on egg production.

CHICORY (*Cichorium intybus*)

Of all the plants available to the farmer, none provides a richer source of all the minerals and trace-elements, vitamins and plant hormones than chicory.

Its thick tap root penetrates, during the normal period of the pasture, a depth of anything up to ten feet, gathering and transmitting to its stem and leaves all the known minerals and microelements necessary for animal health and fertility.

Chicory will grow anywhere. Its deep roots will seek out its own nutritional and moisture requirements over a wide area and great depth, resulting in its survival under almost any conditions. It does not, however, tolerate excessively wet conditions over long periods in its early stages; but short of its young roots standing in water for months it can nevertheless survive longer under such conditions than most other deep-rooting herbs. One field of herbal ley which went into its first winter with a full complement of all the herbs, though the amount of chicory present somewhat reduced, it was the only herb that survived almost four months either under water or with a very high water-level.

Similarly, chicory will continue to push up green leaves almost as fast as it is grazed, when everything else is burnt up by drought. The last drought summer we experienced in Britain, in 1949 and now, the drought in September 1955 sees my herbal leys still lush to confirm the following story. Every pasture in the district—and throughout the country, as far as I was able to observe—was burnt brown, yet my herbal ley continued green and productive throughout the summer. That particular year my grazing ley adjoined a public road, and many passing farmers asked me what fertilizer I had dressed the field with to keep it growing green while theirs, which had been 'given all the sulphate of ammonia we can afford to keep it going' was like an old parched board cracking open with dry rot.

The field had been given nothing but a light dressing of compost—about five tons an acre—in the previous year, but apart from that had nothing even to sow it down with; and yet, in the worst year of drought I have ever known, this pasture maintained my dairy herd, without supplementary feeding—while neighbours were dipping into their winter hay to keep the cows alive. It was solely by virtue of the large proportion of chicory in the mixture that this ley remained evergreen throughout that scorching summer.

Incidentally, an interesting little postscript to this story indicates the ignorance of some of our advisory experts. Because of some carelessness in cleaning the milking machine during the very hot weather of the late summer of that year, we had one or two bad samples of milk and the milk advisory officer for the district was sent to advise me about tracing the cause and avoiding future trouble. She found that the machine was perfectly clean and there was no apparent explanation of the trouble. However, shortly after I'd said good-bye to her she returned to say she thought she'd found the cause of the trouble. 'I notice your cows are grazing the field by the road which has got a lot of blue-flowered weeds in it. *They* no doubt, are affecting the keeping-quality of the milk. I really think you will have to do something about getting rid of those weeds,' she said.

'Well, I don't think even an ultimatum from the Agricultural Committee could compel me to do that,' I replied, 'considering that "those weeds" are chicory which I deliberately sowed in the field. At this time of year it tends to go up to flower if not topped off with a mower.'

"Oh, I'm sorry,' said the dairy-farming expert, 'I hadn't realized chicory had a blue flower, and I thought the leaves around it were dandelions.'

In fact she thought I had a thoroughly weedy field, and it was time I got it cleaned or had a bullying letter from the Agricultural Executive Committee.

I heard no more about milk samples that summer; and there are now many more pastures in the district which show a few blue flowers in late summer.

It is partly this untidy habit of pushing up flowering stems as the grazing season advances that gives chicory its value to soil fertility. For to top these stems and flowers off with a mower feeds back to the top soil precious minerals and trace elements, and who knows what else, that have been brought up from the deep subsoil by the tap roots and crystallized in the leaves, stems and flowers. These supply the health and fertility needs of the grazing cattle, who drop the surplus to the soil in the form of dung; then what they do not graze is fed back to the soil direct by mowing off and letting it remain as a surface mulch.

In this way the trace-mineral content of the top soil is gradually built up over the life of the ley. This process is contributed to by all the deep-rooting herbs in the ley; but chicory is the biggest supplier of this free natural trace-mineral application.

SHEEP'S PARSLEY (*Petroselinum sativum*)

Medicinally this plant is one of the most valuable; and though its use is now advocated in herbal strips, and occasionally in mixtures, the amounts usually recommended are in my experience not half enough because it often suffers from overgrazing.

Besides being highly mineral-rich, it is rich in an element called apiol, which is extracted from some varieties of cultivated parsley for its potent beneficial effect on kidney and bladder complaints. It is also a specific in female reproductive disorders, and should be used in larger seedings where breeding troubles exist in the dairy herd.

Iron and all the known vitamins are also in good quantity in this valuable herb.

Watch the eagerness with which it is grazed by cattle and you will know its great value. In comparative tests I carried out, it proved to be one of the first to be grazed bare where a free choice of individual plots of thirty-five different herbs, grasses and clovers was allowed.

Collect it for your own household salads, and soups too: though it is better in salads, for its rich vitamin content is lost by cooking in soups.

It is my favourite raw snack when I'm out among the cattle grazing my leys; and I can rarely resist a refreshing nibble with them on a hot summer day.

FENNEL (*Foeniculum vulgare*)

As a digestive tonic and bloat-preventive fennel should find a place in every grazing ley. But its seed is not yet available commercially in any quantity, and if not grazed hard it tends to run up to a thick stem and make haymaking, even on tripods, extremely difficult. As seed becomes available it ought nevertheless to be included in herbal strips.

Like Caraway and Dill (of the same family) it has a marked effect in aiding the digestion of an otherwise rich diet; and the cultivation of a little fennel, to be dried for use with a concentrate ration would be a service to the cow's digestive system and a lengthener of her productive life.

CARAWAY (*Carum Carvi*)

The seed of this plant was once widely used in the kitchen as a digestive tonic, both in the famous Caraway Cake—or Seed Cake of our grandmothers—and as a medicine in digestive troubles. It still has great value as a human medicine for dyspepsia, its properties are now finding value in the herbal ley for its ability to aid the digestion of other ingredients of the animal diet—and to encourage the right bacterial flora in the stomach. It is consequently an important anti-bloat ingredient.

Its strong flavour makes it unwise to include more than 1 lb. per acre in the mixture ($^1/_2$ lb. is adequate in case of short supplies), in which proportion it is readily eaten by all classes of farm animals along with the mixture.

SWEET CLOVER—*Melilotus Alba* (WHITE)

Melilotus Officinalis (Yellow) and *Melilotus Altissima* (Yellow) are smaller and less productive wild varieties.

For the improvement of poor soils Sweet Clover has no equal. Sown on its own, or with a grass, it produces great bulk of green manure and a tremendous rooting system. It has a thick tap root which opens up the subsoil, letting in the air and facilitating earthworm and aerobic bacterial activity. In addition to a large quantity of the products of its own root decay after maturity, sweet clover has the ability of all legumes to fix atmospheric nitrogen; and because of its great length and number of roots, Sweet Clover gathers more nitrogen to the soil than most crops.

The Ohio Agricultural Experimental Station reported in Special Circular 53, 1938, that in an official test Sweet Clover sown in the spring with oats—i.e. undersown in spring oats—by November of the same year had contributed nearly a ton an acre of roots, showing a 3.5 percent nitrogen content, to the soil of that field. Sweet Clover hay harvested in the following June, yielded nearly three tons of dry hay containing 2.35 percent of nitrogen.

No crop which has Sweet Clover to precede it, or sown under it (or a ley including it), needs any synthetic nitrogen. It will gather each summer all the nitrogen that can usefully be employed by any crop, and leave a large residue for subsequent years.

An application of sulphate of ammonia to equal the root nitrogen of an acre of Sweet Clover would be $6^3/_4$ cwt. in order to achieve the equivalent application of 76 lb. an acre of crude nitrogen. If the following green crop were incorporated in the top-soil there would be a further application of 140 lb. an acre of nitrogen: equivalent to 13 cwt. an acre of sulphate of ammonia, and nearly ten tons an acre of organic matter with phosphates and potash greater than an equivalent dressing of farmyard manure.

I am convinced, then, that nothing equals sweet clover as a green manure, in preparation for a straw crop and as a pretreatment before seeding down to a long ley. The method of using Sweet Clover for this purpose is described in Chapter XI—*Establishing the Ley.*

American scientists have confirmed the value of sweet clover for manurial purposes in experiments reported in 1943 by O. H. Sears and W. L. Burlison in the Illinois Agricultural Extension Service Circular No. 559 and I. J. Johnson writing in *The Farm Science Reporter* in 1945.

Johnson reported that in experiments in Iowa, Sweet Clover sown in corn followed by oats, repeating the two-year rotation over a sixteen-year period, produced an increase in the yield of corn of 13.8 percent over controlled plots which had no Sweet Clover.

Sears and Burlison report that the use of Sweet Clover as a green manure to follow corn and wheat in a three-year rotation of corn (i.e. maize), oats or wheat, corn, in spite of successive straw crops increased the second crop corn yield from 59 bushels to 80 bushels an acre. In this experiment the corn stalks and wheat straw were returned to the soil with the Sweet Clover.

Who would go to the expense of purchased fertilizers and the labour of applying them in these tightening days, with such rich manurial value available free of charge?

26. A simple mixture of grasses and clovers ten days after mowing. The lower white clover had, of course escaped the mower.

27. A fertility pasture ten days after mowing (in the same field and mown at the same time as the field in plate 26 above). Photograph taken at the height of the 1955 drought. Note quick recovery of the deep rooting herbs.

28. American sweet clover.

29. Yarrow in the herbal ley.

Sweet Clover is not advisable as a solo forage crop, because it is slightly bitter and unpalatable on its own, owing to a toxin called coumarin which is present in the plant and which the animals do not readily accustom themselves to, and which is an anticoagulant causing the animal, if injured or scratched, to be liable to bleed to death. This property of melilot is being used in the treatment of human thrombosis to prevent the formation of blood clots.

But American plant breeders, who value the great productive capacity of Sweet Clover, are attempting to breed a strain of the crop with a reduced coumarin content which will make it one of our most profitable forage crops.

Meanwhile, it is still a valuable ingredient of leys, especially on poor and calcareous soils, up to 4-7 lb. an acre. There is scope for experiment with Sweet Clover as a major companion crop for silage purposes—possibly grown in equal quantities with Cocksfoot, Timothy or Meadow Fescue and Lucerne or another legume such as Trifolium, or Red Clover.

CHAPTER XVI

The Character & Properties of Grasses

ITALIAN RYEGRASS

Italian Ryegrass is perhaps the most widely used and the most useful of grasses for ley farming. Though its life is short, its adaptability to a wide range of conditions, its quick growing nature and its winter hardiness, make it suitable as an ingredient for all leys, long or short. In the long ley it gives the first grazing in the first and second years ; in the short ley it produces a quick bulk for mowing, and an aftermath for ploughing or discing in.

The greatest virtue of Italian Ryegrass (and in these general terms I include the more recent grasses, Westerwolth's Ryegrass and New Zealand H.I. strain, Short Rotation Ryegrass) is that it is possible, by planning sowings, to obtain grazing at any time of winter or summer at a predetermined period after sowing. I found in experimenting with these grasses that, assuming reasonably normal growing weather, (and that means primarily sufficient moisture), whether in early spring or late summer one can arrange to have a bulk of grazing at almost any time by sowing a mixture in which one of these grasses predominates, approximately eight weeks before it is needed for grazing during the period March to September. Even for grazing during the period October to March, a sowing in late August or early September can produce, provided a sufficient area is sown to allow for the fact that regrowth may not be expected after grazing in December, a continuous winter grazing excepting, of course, during a period when the ground is completely covered with snow (though even then cattle will find it under the snow if it is long enough).

144

The disadvantage of this continuous grazing system is, of course, that none of these ryegrasses last beyond the second year, at any rate in economical quantities: so that a system of continuous grazing, based on ryegrasses, involves a continuous rotation of sowings ; and it is probably more economical to devise fewer mixtures, designed to give grazing at different times of the year, but to remain down for a period of four years.

All leys, whether of short- or long-term, should include, in my experience, at least 6 lb. of one of the species of *Lolium Italicum:* that is, either the simple *Lolium Italicum* or *Lolium Itaticum* variety *Westerwoldicum* or the New Zealand Short rotation strain.

The simple Italian Ryegrass is available in a number of commercial strains: Irish, American and Danish, or in the more leafy strain, Aberystwyth S.22.

Westerwolth's Ryegrass is, strictly speaking, not a biennial grass, though it will produce quite considerable growth in the second year, and if allowed to go to seed will grow quite as strongly in the second year as in the first. The main feature of Westerwolth's Ryegrass is its speed of growth and the extreme bulkiness which it produces ; but I do not favour this grass for grazing purposes because it tends to be rather stemmy and lacking in leaf, except in the very early stages of growth. The chief use to which I have put it is with a mixture of Broad Red Clover and Chicory in building up the fertility of very poor fields. It produces the quickest and greatest bulk of all grasses ; and in combination with Red Clover and Chicory gives an excellent bulky green manure for discing into the top soil to provide humus and nitrogen, and in the process of growth and subsequent discing-in to aid the elimination of weeds, and with the acids of its own decay release additional minerals which are unavailable in humus-deficient soils.

New Zealand Short Rotation Ryegrass, H.1 Strain

This is the most recent of Ryegrasses; and as far as my experience of it goes it appears to be the most leafy and productive. It is much more palatable than Westerwolth's Ryegrass and as palatable as the ordinary Italian Ryegrass. It is much later to go to seed than all other strains of Italian Ryegrass that I have used—even the Aberystwyth S.22, which is a leafy, late-flowering strain. Short Rotation Ryegrass also lasts longer under good soil conditions and grazing management than any of the other annual or biennial ryegrasses. This is probably due to the fact that it was bred from a cross between Perennial and Italian Ryegrass, and seems to have inherited the longer life of the Perennial Ryegrass and the quick growth and palatability of Italian Ryegrass. It provides the earliest grazing of all grasses in the spring; and when sown in early autumn will provide grazing and continual growth throughout the winter, except in the most extreme conditions of cold. It forms the basis of my mixtures for early spring and winter grazing.

Any one of these three short-term ryegrasses may be sown with confidence on any type of soil. I have found they thrive equally well on light and heavy soil and in moist and dry conditions; and no mixture should be without one of them, to provide early cover for the other ingredients of longer leys and the first grazing while the remaining ingredients are being established.

PERENNIAL RYEGRASS *(Lolium Perenne)*

Perennial Ryegrass is the next-most-commonly used of ryegrasses and is included in all seeds mixtures, long or short. But poor strains of Perennial Ryegrass, especially under conditions of low fertility in the soil, grow to resemble the tines of a Ferguson Scratcher—and are just about as palatable and little more nutritious. This probably explains Robert Elliot's violent adverse opinions of Perennial Ryegrass, for in his day there were no pedigree, leafy strains, and most ryegrasses available at that time required a very high degree of fertility to prevent them from going quickly to stem and seed: for none of them had been selected for leafiness and palatability. Even to-day, Perennial Ryegrass is not one of the most acceptable grazing grasses where cattle have a choice under conditions of low fertility. Its palatability is much improved by maintaining a high organic content in the soil, and providing it with a wide variety of companion herbs and clovers. It is essential, of course, to use only the improved pedigree strains, of which there are several designed for various purposes.

ABERYSTWYTH S.23 PERENNIAL RYEGRASS

This is the most widely used strain of ryegrass designed primarily for grazing purposes. Though rather later to growth in the spring, it is slow to come to flower; and provides a great bulk of extremely leafy grass up to midsummer, and again during the autumn and winter. It is very persistent and will out-live most other ingredients of the long-term ley. Ideally, it must have a good proportion of clovers and grows best with its stablemate, S.100 White Clover—which provides, by process of nitrogen fixa-

30. American sweet clover (*Melilotus Alba*).

31. Broad-leaved plantain (*Plantago Major*).

tion in the root-nodules of the clover which is ultimately transmitted in the soil to the ryegrass, the excessively large quantities of nitrogen upon which this strain of ryegrass thrives best. In my opinion, arising from personal experience and the observation of many other leys, this is the only satisfactory way of providing the necessary nitrogen for maximum growth of Perennial Ryegrass in such a way as to maintain its palatability to livestock. Ryegrass, when stimulated with nitrogenous fertilizers, unquestionably produces large quantities of grass. But observation of cattle grazing predominantly ryegrass leys, manured with large quantities of nitrogenous fertilizers which tend to depress the clovers and decrease the action of nitrifying bacteria, when compared with similar leys in which the clovers are encouraged by close grazing and suitable resting periods, leaves no doubt that the grazing animal prefers the latter. I am equally convinced that the extra bulk of ryegrass which may be produced from nitrogenous fertilizers does not produce a proportionate increase in milk yield. The blue sheen on ryegrass, which follows the excessive use of sulphate of ammonia displays to his neighbours the farmer who will reap in his cattle the self-sown disease of his greed. I have never yet walked through the deep green-blue of an over-stimulated Perennial Ryegrass ley without finding, in the cattle which graze it, breeding troubles, acetonaemia and other forms of protein poisoning. Perennial Ryegrass, manured organically and grazed judiciously, is the loyal grass which lasts long in the ley; but, if whipped with the nitrogen bag, hits back with a poisoned blade.

The Aberystwyth S.23 strain, in particular, when grown in conjunction with S.100 clover, if grazed too hard for long periods, will tend to submit to the domination of the clover. It is wise, therefore, to graze for shorter periods, allowing reasonably long rest periods for the S.23 Ryegrass to establish itself and maintain equality with the clover. An occasional opportunity during the year for the ryegrass to grow almost to maturity by taking a cut of hay or silage, especially in the second and third year, will enable it to maintain its position in competition with the clovers in the ley.

ABERYSTWYTH S.101 PERENNIAL RYEGRASS

Because the S.23 strain of ryegrass does not provide much grazing during midsummer, an alternative strain for use in leys designed primarily for summer grazing is the S.101 strain. This flowers later, produces little growth in the spring, but gives a good bulk of extremely leafy herbage during the period around midsummer. For this reason it is also a good variety for hay and silage mixtures where the cut is to be taken rather late. I have not considered it of particular virtue in the general-purpose ley; but where a mixture is being sown to meet the shortage of the July-August period there is a case for the inclusion of 5 or 6 lb. of S.101.

ABERYSTWYTH S.24 PERENNIAL RYEGRASS

This strain of Perennial Ryegrass is primarily for haymaking purposes, but is leafier than the commercial or New Zealand strains of ryegrass. I would include it only where it is intended to cut hay, in preference to grazing, in the ley of not more than three years' duration: for the longer ley of complex mixture I have not found that S.24 has a place of any value. Similarly, *New Zealand Certified Perennial Ryegrass* is useful only in the shorter leys designed for haymaking purposes.

COCKSFOOT OR ORCHARD GRASS (*Dactylis Glomerata*)

Cocksfoot is one of the most productive of grasses; and also one of the most useful on all soils when properly managed; but no one should grow much cocksfoot in his ley mixtures unless he can be sure of being able to control it with a large number of cattle and a good mower knife.

Given kindly treatment in its first year, to enable it to become properly established, it will, in the latter part of the first year and subsequent years, stand very heavy grazing; indeed it is essential that it should be grazed hard at all times to prevent it from gaining predominance in the sward or becoming unpalatable to stock. In its young leafy stages it is relished by cattle as much as any other domestic crop; but once it becomes stemmy and the leaves become coarse, stock will not touch it and it quickly goes to seed and develops a tufty growth.

In my book, *Fertility Farming,* I suggested heavy seedings of Cocksfoot, in order to prevent the inevitable tuftiness which is associated with this grass. I have since discovered that the amount of seed in relation to the subsequent evenness of the cocksfoot in the sward is not so important as grazing it hard, and keeping it short either by grazing it or by use of the mower during the whole season. Once established, I know of no grass which will tolerate such heavy grazing or continuous mowing as Cocksfoot. No grass is quicker to put forth a fresh leafy growth after grazing or mowing than Cocksfoot if allowed a short rest. It is often suggested that it will not tolerate much grazing in the early part of the year; but provided it is not poached in the winter too much (and if this is done ultimate tuftiness is inevitable) it comes early in the spring, and will stand quite heavy grazing for the rest of the year, recovering quickly after grazing. If the grazing is not heavy enough to keep it in control it is most important to follow the cattle immediately with the mower: otherwise, should it go to seed, no stock will touch it, and hard, coarse clumps develop. This is probably because the grass does not appear to spread evenly over the ground in the way other grasses do, but develops a hard-core centre to each plant, which becomes impossible to maintain in a level condition once it has developed.

Cocksfoot is a deep-rooting grass and will continue to show fresh green growth while other grasses are burnt up by drought. For this reason it is an admirable companion for the deep-rooting herbs of the herbal ley and should always find a place in the herbal ley mixture. Similarly, Cocksfoot shows great benefit from its association with clovers, being a lover of nitrogen, which is supplied by the nitrifying bacteria of the root-nodules of the legume.

In my observation of the ingredients of the bulky growth of the hedgerows I saw that Cocksfoot invariably predominates. This is a clue which should not be overlooked in aiming at maximum production of the kind which is available under the natural conditions of the hedgerow in the early season. It is also an indication that under conditions of high fertility, which results from the plentiful organic matter of the hedgerow and organically-farmed land, Cocksfoot is one of the most desirable of grasses.

An additional point in its favour is that it shows greater benefit from good soil conditions than probably any other grass. Under very poor conditions it grows coarse and fibrous; but where the fertility is high its nutritional value and palatability are equal to any other grass. Cocksfoot has gained the reputation for being coarse, fibrous and often unpalatable, largely because of bad methods of management, particularly on the poorer soils. Given a high content of organic matter in the soil in which it is grown, it produces a highly nutritious and acceptable grazing for all classes of livestock; and because of its low moisture content compared with other grasses, produces a great bulk of dry matter, which, under good conditions of soil fertility, and in conjunction with a wide variety of herbs, makes a greater contribution to the total yield of nutriment from the ley than any other grass.

No grass demonstrates better than Cocksfoot the use of the mower in maintaining the condition and nutritive value of a ley. On an acre plot of Cocksfoot and Lucerne, which I had grown experimentally and in which the Lucerne had almost disappeared, due partly to poor establishment under the conditions in which it was sown, the crop was now almost predominantly cocksfoot. After one grazing and one cut, which went into silage, the third growth was allowed to grow up to about 6 in. in height. A section of it was then mown for feeding green to cattle indoors, and the whole was then left for three weeks. During that three weeks there was a good deal of rain and the growing conditions were good, though the time was September. Surprisingly, during that time the mown portion of the Cocksfoot grew so fast that it became level in height with the remainder of the plot, which had not been mown or touched in any way since the growth of the whole field had reached 6 in.

When the cattle were allowed to graze the whole of this cocksfoot they almost completely ignored the unmown portion until the mown portion had been grazed thoroughly, though the two sections were approximately the same length of growth.

This demonstrates not only the improved palatability of the younger growth following topping-off with a mower, but also the very quick recovery of Cocksfoot after mowing, provided a satisfactory rest period is allowed, even though the end of the normal grazing season is being approached.

It also shows how much is lost when a pasture is not frequently grazed or mown but left to grow to maturity. Certainly with Cocksfoot and many other species the more you cut the more you get.

Of the various varieties of Cocksfoot, Danish Cocksfoot, which is primarily a hay strain, is the earliest to grow in the spring; and for early grazing purposes a mixture might well include a small proportion of the commercial Danish strain, but for all other purposes there is no point in using this strain where the specially bred pedigree strains of leafy Cocksfoot are available.

Of the pedigree pasture strains of Cocksfoot I have always found a combination of Aberystwyth S.26 and Aberystwyth S.143 gives the best results and, especially where separate mixtures are used for early grazing, there is no point whatever in including the purely hay strains of Cocksfoot, such as the Danish or the New Zealand strains in a general-purpose mixture. S.26, being a hay-pasture strain, comes quite early enough to provide a good cut of hay; and at the normal time for haymaking provides a leafier and more nutritious hay than the so-called purely hay strains of the grass. These pedigree strains of Cocksfoot, though they will grow on the poorest of soils where other grasses may not prosper, nevertheless benefit from organic manures in a remarkable way; and on all except the heaviest and most intractable clays I would always include a few pounds of Aberystwyth S.26 and Aberystwyth S.143 Cocksfoot.

TIMOTHY (*Phleum pratense*) sometimes known as Catstail.

Timothy grass is, with Cocksfoot, perhaps the highest in dry matter content of all grasses. Though rather slower to establish than Cocksfoot or Italian Ryegrass it favours a wide range of soils, with special preference for heavy damp soils and should be preferred to Cocksfoot on the heaviest soils.

Because I have found Timothy tends to be rather shy in competition with Cocksfoot, I think it is wise to sow rather more Timothy than Cocksfoot in mixtures where they are both included. Subsequent management, too, must also maintain a balance between these two grasses, by not allowing the ley to grow so far that the Cocksfoot predominates. Normal grazing and topping off with a mower after grazing, will be sufficient to maintain a balance; but where repeated hay crops are taken, allowing the grasses to grow to maturity, the clocksfoot tends to gain the upper hand.

Timothy does not contribute so abundantly to the first year's grazing as, for instance, Perennial Ryegrass or Cocksfoot, as it is somewhat slow to establish; but in later years it provides an extremely heavy yield of very palatable and nutritious grass. Under heavy grazing, especially where long rest periods are not possible, I have found the commercial strains of Timothy very quickly die out before the end of a four- or five-year ley; but the pedigree strains have shown a great improvement in this respect, and the following varieties can be relied upon to survive the heaviest grazing with either cattle or sheep.

ABERYSTWYTH S.48 AND S.50

I have included these two strains together as they are both purely pasture types of Timothy. The S.50 is an extreme pasture type, bred solely for grazing purposes. It is prostrate and covers the ground by its spreading habit of growth, providing a dense sward when grown in conjunction with the Aberystwyth S.48. The S.48 is more upright in growth and to be preferred to S.50 where the grass is to be cut for hay, though the S.51 is the pure hay strain and might be included where the ley is designed as much for hay as for grazing. In my own experience I prefer to sow a primarily grazing ley, and to take the hay or silage at periods when the grass is growing beyond the cows. For this reason I find S.48 quite adequate, in conjunction with the other grasses, as a provider of hay; and it gives more scope for lengthening the period in which hay can be taken. This does not mean that we take hay when the grass is not at its best, but that S.48 is, in my experience, more palatable and nutritious for a longer period than S.51, because S.51 more quickly goes to seed. All strains of Timothy, being yielders of bulky, broad leaves, benefit greatly from organic manuring; or, failing that, the topping-off with a mower each year of a little of its own growth. The broader-leafed grasses, as welas the herbs, show a wonderful response to a feed of even the smallest quantity of the ley mixture itself in combination with the dung and urine which has been left by the grazing animal. Hence the great importance of frequent topping with the mower and harrowing with the chain harrows, or a 'scratcher' of some kind, following grazing; and, if possible, a topping-off which provides something more than the occasional long stalk which has been left ungrazed because of its unpalatability. I believe more and more that to remove the grazing animal a little before the field is bare, when topping is to be done, well repays the little grazing that may have been lost when the ultimate growth which results from it comes along.

MEADOW FESCUE (*Festuca pratensis*)

Meadow Fescue is becoming increasingly popular as an ingredient of the simpler mixtures because, where choice is limited to one or two grasses, it is one of the most nutritious. It is a slow starter, but very productive; and once established is a heavy cropper. Unfortunately it is not, in my experience, as productive or palatable as Timothy on heavy soils where it is used as an alternative to Timothy as the companion grass for Lucerne. I would not, therefore, use it alone with Lucerne in the way that is widely advocated by some authorities. But it is worth a prominent place in all ley mixtures, for it produces an abundant growth in July and August when the ryegrasses are at their lowest. It does not compete well with ryegrasses in the earlier summer; but when they are grazed back, Meadow Fescue will come in to take the place of the ryegrasses, provided it has not been obliterated by the ryegrasses.

Meadow Fescue prefers a very heavy soil, but grows well on all soils of medium to good fertility. It prospers better alongside Timothy than Perennial Ryegrass; and it would be worth while experimenting with a drastic reduction of Perennial Ryegrass on the heavier soils, and growing Timothy and Meadow Fescue as the two main grasses in leys of five or six years'

32. Yarrow, chicory, sheep's parsley, cocksfoot, H.I. ryegrass, S.100 white clover, late-flowering red clover.

33. Kidney vetch.

duration. Meadow Fescue is not really at its best until the third year, so of necessity in my four-year leys I have limited it in favour of the quicker establishing grasses.

Meadow Fescue is, however, one of the best for winter growth, and should always take a predominant place in a mixture to be kept down a number of years, primarily for the purpose of providing winter grazing.

TALL FESCUE (*Festuca elatior*)

Tall fescue is a taller growing and broader leaved grass than Meadow Fescue. It has a long growing season and in good conditions of soil and moisture will remain green throughout summer and winter. It tends to be unpalatable on soils of low fertility, but is one of the deepest rooting of grasses, which makes it a valuable ingredient of mixtures on all types of soil.

All the above grasses are temporary ley grasses with a fairly tall and up-right growth. In a ley of not more than four years' duration it is not worth while spending money on the 'bottom' grasses. The S.100 and Wild White Clover can be relied on to fill up the bottom of the ley; but for longer leys and permanent pastures the shorter and finer bottom grasses are worth including if they can be bought at reasonable prices. They are:

ROUGH STALKED MEADOW GRASS (*Poa Trivialis*)

This grass grows well on the moister soils. It grows on the poorest soils, given sufficient moisture. It is in somewhat short supply, however—and seed may be costly. But in the longer ley it fills the undergrowth well with only 1 lb. an acre.

CRESTED DOGSTAIL (*Cynosurus cristatus*)

This is one of the best drought-resisters I know, and is always worth a place in the very dry areas. I make little use of it now because, except for the occasional summer—such as 1949 (which was the last really dry one we had, when it served me well) we are not, it seems, much troubled by too little moisture in the summer in my part of the world.

THE CHARACTERS AND PROPERTIES

MEADOW FOXTAIL (*Alopecurus pratensis*)

This is not a bottom grass; it grows two or three feet high if allowed to go to maturity, but it is included in this section as a permanent rather than a temporary ley ingredient; for it is not in full production until its third year, so is of no real value in the four-year ley. At its present price, which at the time of writing is 12s. 6d. a lb., it is not worth serious consideration.

HARD FESCUE (*Festuca durusicula*)

In my experience this grass is suitable only for permanent or long duration pastures, when it provides an undergrowth of very fine, almost hair-thin, leaf. Again, its expense limits its use except in special mixtures. It can be used with advantage in a ley of five to seven years' duration to be used primarily for poultry, as it has a succulent leaf much liked by poultry.

SMOOTH STALKED MEADOW GRASS OR KENTUCKY BLUE GRASS (*Poa Pratensis*)

This grass is scarce and expensive in Britain, and consequently little used. But it is an extremely popular and very productive grass in the United States. Enthusiasts for their Kentucky Blue Grass, as it is best known in America, have sent me supplies of seed; and I must say it is an abundant cropper which seems to deserve more attention here. It has a creeping root and early growth, and favours the lighter drier soils.

*   *   *

Neither this chapter on grasses, nor the previous one on herbs pretends to be in any way complete. I have not attempted to describe varieties with which I have no experience. But for the purposes of ley farming and the establishment of good fertility pastures I believe it to be adequate.

As I gain experience of further herbs, grasses and legumes I shall add them to later editions of this book.

CHAPTER XVII

Herbal Ley Mixtures

And some Silage, Dredge Corn, and Winter Grazing Mixtures

A ll the herbal ley mixtures in this section are suitable for use as four-year leys where it is usual to break the ley after four years. Three years is too short a period in which to derive maximum benefit either in yield of grass or soil fertility; and I consider four or five years the optimum life. Each mixture is, however, basically also a permanent pasture mixture, so may be left down longer if necessary.

The quantities of seeds making up the mixtures are the ideal for quick establishment and soil coverage; but where extra economy is necessary in seasons of high-priced seeds, the eventual pasture, though slower to 'fill up,' will be ultimately just as good with up to a third less seed, thus reducing the cost by one-third. But soil conditions, seedbed and fertility must be perfect for this reduction of seed quantity.

EARLY-GRAZING HERBAL LEY

(which also produces well throughout the summer)

	lb.per acre
Perennial Ryegrass, S.24	3
Irish or Ayrshire Ryegrass	3
Cocksfoot Danish	4
Cocksfoot, S.191	4
Short Rotation Ryegrass, New Zealand H.1	6
Clover, S.100	1
Broad Red Clover	2
Meadow Fescue, S.215	4

HERBAL LEY MIXTURES

	lb.per acre
Tall Fescue	2
Chicory (*Cichorium intybus*)	3
Sheep's Parsley (*Petroselinum sativum*)	2
Lucerne	2
American Sweet Clover (*Melilotus Alba*)	2
Ribgrass or long-leaved Plantain	2
Caraway (*Carum Carvi*)	1
Broad-leaved Plantain (*Plantago major*)	1
	42

This is the mixture of grasses and herbs which I have found give the earliest growth of the spring. Getting 'early bite' is usually reckoned to be largely a matter of laying on the nitrogen. Many farmers have fallen for this fallacy and *themselves* provided 'early bite' for the fertilizer salesmen. Once bitten, the more careful and intelligent farmers are twice shy of the soft, watery-growth admittedly earlier to come to the cow's mouth, but so often faster to flow from just beneath her tail. Scouring cows benefit little from this expensive form of protein-poisoning—and

the slow subsequent growth from a ley which has been forced with nitrogenous fertilizers for the much-boosted 'early bite' makes it as wasteful of the farmer's cash as it is of the cow's health.

Wholesome, substantial and nutritious early bite may be obtained from a specially selected seeds mixture grown in one of the more sheltered fields of the farm, given if possible a light dressing of organic manure in the winter—or a thin sprinkling of straw to act as a gentle cloche to keep the grass warm and give it an early start.

Early bite obtained in this way will not scour the cows or rob the field of its ability to recover quickly after being grazed, and will maintain reasonable growth without expensive stimulants during the rest of the year.

34. Chickory.

35. Burnet.

36. Cocksfoot.

37. Lucerne (alfalfa) and Timothy grass.

38. On the right, deep-rooting herbal ley mixture on land formerly incapable (because of stone and rock near surface) of growing a corn crop — see poor oat crop on left.

39. A close up of a fertility pasture showing yarrow and plantain among the clovers and grasses.

Midsummer-Grazing Herbal Ley Mixture

(For July and August Summer Growth)

	lb. an acre
Lucerne	6
Chicory	6
Timothy, S.48	3
Timothy, S.50	3
Clover, S.100	1
Burnet *(Poterium sanguisorba)*	3
Late-flowering Red Clover	2
Meadow Fescue, S.53	4
Perennial Ryegrass, S.101	6
Perennial Ryegrass, S.23	6
American Sweet Clover	2
Sheep's Parsley	2
Caraway	1
Ribgrass (Long-leaved Plantain)	1
Broad-leaved Plantain	1
	47

Though this mixture is at its best in the semi-drought conditions of midsummer, and provides maximum grazing during the period of grass shortage on most farms, it does also provide good grazing throughout the normal growing season. The inclusion of an unusually high seeding of Chicory, and rather more of the deeper-rooting legumes, Lucerne and Sweet Clover, gives it remarkable powers of recovery after grazing during a period of drought.

It is best, therefore, grazed or mown during May and early June—being left to receive its heavy grazing in July and August, August when less specialized mixtures show little or no growth.

HERBAL LEY MIXTURE FOR AUTUMN AND WINTER GRAZING

	lb. an acre
Cocksfoot, S.26	4
Perennial Ryegrass, S.23	8
Timothy, S.48	6
Red Fescue, S.59	3
Ribgrass (Long-leaved Plantain)	2
Clover, S.100	1
Chicory	2
Lucerne	2
Caraway	1
Broad-leaved Plantain	1
Burnet	3
	33

Though there has in recent years been quite a vogue for what is called 'foggage' for winter grazing, my experience has been that this coarse brown growth which results from leaving August and September growth for winter grazing has little more than belly-filling value. It is no good for milk-production or fattening when it has become so fibrous, colourless, and dry as foggage does from the Cocksfoot usually predominant ley used for that purpose.

The above mixture is chosen from grasses and herbs which I have observed growing later into the autumn and winter than other varieties or strains. If rested from mid-September this mixture will remain green and growing (if only slightly) through the winter, except in the most exposed positions.

The most important factor in achieving winter growth is a high organic content in the soil to maintain a higher temperature. If possible, give a light dressing of organic manure—say five tons to the acre of compost, or 3 to 5 cwt. to the acre of a more concentrated sewage powder or seaweed fertilizer (or combination of the two) before resting the field in September. This will set in motion the vigorous bacterial activity which creates the warmth and nutriment necessary to winter growth. In any case, allow a three-inch growth during the summer to be mown and left to lie on the surface. This will act as a cloche to warm the soil and feed the winter growth, while it slowly decomposes around the roots of the new green growth that is so valuable in the winter.

HERBAL LEY MIXTURE FOR VERY THIN, DRY SOILS

(and to resist extreme drought conditions)

	lb. an acre
Cocksfoot, S.143	5
Crested Dogstail	4
Tall Fescue	4
Lucerne	4
Kidney Vetch	4
Chicory	4
Burnet	4
Ribgrass or Plantain	4
Late-flowering Red Clover	2
Alsike	2
Trefoil	2
Clover, S.100 White	1
Yarrow	½
American Sweet Clover	2
Broad-leaved Plantain	1
	43½

The main essential of a mixture for thin soils, soils overlying and close to the rock, and in excessively dry countries, is that it should contain a predominance of the deepest-rooting varieties available, consistent with their production above the ground. This makes the most of such little moisture as is present in the deeper subsoil; and where the subsoil is largely rock some penetration of the rock can be achieved by the more powerful of the deeper rooters.

Every one of the ingredients of this mixture is an exceptionally deep rooter, except the clovers S.100, Trefoil, Alsike and Late-flowering Red—and even Alsike and Trefoil and reasonably drought-resistant. All prosper on the thinnest soils; but the mixture is not ideal for good deep soils.

HERBAL LEY MIXTURES

LUCERNE OR ALFALFA MIXTURES

Lucerne Pastures for Silage or Grazing

Heavy Moist Soil

	lb. an acre
Lucerne or Alfalfa	10
Late-flowering Red Clover	2
Timothy	4
Chicory	3
Clover, S.100	1
	20

Medium Soil

Lucerne or Alfalfa	10
Late-flowering Red Clover	2
Timothy	4
Meadow Fescue, S.53	3
Chicory	3
Clover, S.100	1
	23

Light Soil

Lucerne or Alfalfa	10
Late-flowering Red Clover	2
Cocksfoot, S.26	5
Chicory	3
Clover, S.100	1
	21

In a wet season, which the lucerne does not enjoy, the Red Clover and S.100, together with the grass, prosper and produce a large bulk. In a very dry season, when the shallower clovers suffer from drought, Lucerne will make up a full crop almost single-handed.

The Chicory will thrive under all conditions.

For silage only, omit S.100 and reduce Red Clover to one pound in each case.

All-Purpose Herbal Ley Mixtures

For all-year grazing where acreage will not allow for special seasonal mixtures.

Suitable for all soils (direct or undersown).

	lb. an acre
Cocksfoot, S.26	3
Cocksfoot, S.143	3
Timothy, S.48	3
Timothy (Aberystwyth, S.51)	3
Meadow Fescue	2
Tall Fescue	1
H.1. Short-Rotation Ryegrass	6
Perennial Ryegrass, S.24	3
Perennial Ryegrass (Aberystwyth, S.23)	3
Burnet	3
Chicory	3
Yarrow	¼
Lucerne	2
Alsike Clover	1
Kidney Vetch	1
Montgomery Late-flowering Red Clover, Certified	1
White Clover (Aberystwyth, S.100)	1
Wild White Clover, New Zealand	½
Sheep's Parsley	3
Sweet Clover	3
Ribgrass (Long-leaved Plantain)	2
Broad-leaved Plantain	1
	48¾

If in any doubt about the type of mixture to sow for any particular conditions or purposes, this mixture provides a foolproof certainty for all conditions, with maximum grazing and mowing yield at all seasons of the year. It will not provide the same growth in out-of-season periods, i.e. early spring, late autumn and winter, as the mixtures I have suggested specifically for these purposes; but it is the best all-round general purpose mixture I have experienced.

HERBAL HEDGEROW MIXTURE

For supplementing existing pastures, particularly for goats.

	lb. an acre
Chicory	1
Sheep's Parsley	1
Burnet	1
Sweet Clover	1
Kidney Vetch	1
Ribgrass (Plantain)	1
Yarrow	¼
	6¼

To be sown in or near the hedgerows at the rate of approximately 6¼ lb. for each one acre of the field.

THE GOOSEGREEN HERBAL LEY MIXTURES

The Goosegreen Herbal Ley Mixtures are a series of general-purpose mixtures which I have developed for maximum production and length of grazing season. None of them is designed for any special time of the year—but all are capable of adaptation by grazing management to provide growth when it is most needed. The wide variety of ingredients has enabled me to shift the maximum growth period according to the time of year at which the early and late varieties are grazed.

Each mixture here listed is varied only to suit different soil conditions or manner of seeding, i.e. with a cover crop or direct.

They are developed from the mixtures recommended in my books, *Fertility Farming* and *Herdsmanship*.

HERBAL LEY MIXTURES
GOOSEGREEN HERBAL LEY (GENERAL PURPOSE)
(including H.1 Ryegrass for direct re-seeding)

	lb. an acre
Perennial Ryegrass, S.23	4
Perennial Ryegrass, S.24	4
Cocksfoot, S.143 } on light soils	4
Cocksfoot, S.26	
	4
Timothy, S.51 } on heavy soils	
or Timothy, S.48	4
	2
Meadow Fescue	
Late-flowering Red Clover	2
(Montgomery or Aberystwyth)	
	1
Tall Fescue	
	1
White Clover, S.100	
Wild White Clover, N.Z.	½
or Kent Indigenous	
	2
Chicory	
	4
Burnet	
	½
Yarrow	
	2
Sheep's Parsley	
	1
Alsike	
American Sweet Clover	2
Kidney Vetch	1
Lucerne	2
Ribgrass (*Plantago Lanceolata*)	1
New Zealand H.1, Short Rotation yegrass	6
Broad-leaved Plantain (*Plantago Major*)	1
	53

171

GOOSEGREEN HERBAL LEY (GENERAL PURPOSE)

(to be undersown in a nurse crop)

	lb. an acre
Perennial Ryegrass, S.23	4
Perennial Ryegrass, S.24	4
Cocksfoot, S.143 } on light soils	3
Cocksfoot, S.26	3
Timothy, S.51 } on heavy soils	
or Timothy, S.48	3
Meadow Fescue	2
Late-flowering Red Clover (Montgomery or Aberystwyth)	2
Tall Fescue	1
White Clover, S.100	1
Wild White Clover, N.Z. or Kent Indigenous	½
Chicory	2
Burnet	4
Yarrow	½
Sheep's Parsley	2
Alsike	1
American Sweet Clover	2
Kidney Vetch	1
Lucerne	2
Ribgrass (*Plantago Lanceolata*)	1
Broad-leaved Plantain (*Plantago Major*)	1
	40

Light Land Herbal Ley

(for direct seeding)

	lb. an acre
Perennial Ryegrass, S.23	4
Perennial Ryegrass, S.24	4
Cocksfoot, S.143	5
Cocksfoot, S.26	5
Meadow Fescue	2
Late-flowering Red Clover (Montgomery or Aberystwyth)	2
Tall Fescue	1
White Clover, S.100	1
Wild White Clover, N.Z. or Kent Indigenous	¼
Chicory	2
Burnet	4
Yarrow	½
Sheep's Parsley	2
Alsike	1
American Sweet Clover	2
Kidney Vetch	1
Lucerne	2
Ribgrass (*Plantago Lanceolata*)	1
Broad-leaved Plantain (*Plantago Major*)	1
New Zealand H.1, Short Rotation Ryegrass	6
	46 ¾

173

HERBAL LEY MIXTURES

LIGHT LAND HERBAL LEY
(to be undersown with a nurse crop)

	lb. an acre
Perennial Ryegrass, S.23	4
Perennial Ryegrass, S.24	4
Cocksfoot, S.143	5
Cocksfoot, S.26	5
Meadow Fescue	2
Late-flowering Red Clover (Montgomery or Aberystwyth)	2
Chicory	2
Burnet	4
Yarrow	¼
Sheep's Parsley	2
Alsike	1
American Sweet Clover	2
Kidney Vetch	1
Lucerne	2
Ribgrass (*Plantago Lanceolata*)	1
Broad-leaved Plantain (*Plantago Major*)	1
	40¾

HEAVY LAND HERBAL LEY
(for direct sowing)

	lb. an acre
Perennial Ryegrass, S.23	4
Perennial Ryegrass, S.24	4
Timothy, S.51	4
Timothy, S.48	4
Meadow Fescue	2
Late-flowering Red Clover (Montgomery or Aberystwyth)	2
Tall Fescue	1
White Clover, S.100	1

HERBAL LEY MIXTURES

	lb. an acre
Wild White Clover, N.Z. or Kent Indigenous	½
Chicory	2
Burnet	4
Yarrow	¼
Sheep's Parsley	2
Alsike	1
American Sweet Clover	2
Kidney Vetch	1
Lucerne	2
Ribgrass (*Plantago Lanceolata*)	1
Broad-leaved Plantain (*Plantago Major*)	1
New Zealand H.1, Short Rotation Ryegrass	6
	44¾

HEAVY LAND HERBAL LEY
(for undersowing)

	lb. an acre
Perennial Ryegrass, S.23	4
Perennial Ryegrass, S.24	4
Timothy, S.51	4
Timothy, S.48	4
Meadow Fescue	2
Late-flowering Red Clover (Montgomery or Aberystwyth)	2
Tall Fescue	1
White Clover, S.100	1
Wild White Clover, N.Z. or Kent Indigenous	½
Chicory	2
Burnet	4
Yarrow	¼
Sheep's Parsley	2
Alsike	1
American Sweet Clover	2

175

	lb. an acre
Lucerne	2
Ribgrass (*Plantago Lanceolata*)	1
Broad-leaved Plantain (*Plantago Major*)	½
	38¼

PIG AND POULTRY LEY

Poultry Ley

	lb. an acre
Perennial Ryegrass, S.23	4
Perennial Ryegrass, S.24	4
Meadow Fescue	2
Late-flowering Red Clover (Montgomery or Aberystwyth)	2
Hard Fescue	1
White Clover, S.100	1
Wild White Clover, N.Z.	1
Chicory	2
Yarrow	¼
Burnet	2
Sheep's Parsley	2
Ribgrass or Plantain	1
Kidney Vetch	1
	23¼

This mixture is made up of the finer, less fibrous grasses, together with the leafy Chicory, Plantain and Kidney Vetch. Yarrow, Burnet, and Sheep's Parsley are all special favourites with poultry, and have a potent beneficial effect on the health and productive capacity of the birds.

The mixture also lends itself well to a combination of poultry-grazing with the closer grazing of sheep or calves.

Pig Grazing Ley

(Ideal for folding or strip-grazing)

	lb. an acre
New Zealand Ryegrass, H.1	4
Meadow Fescue, S.215	3
Timothy (Scandinavian)	2
White Clover, S.100	2
Wild White Clover, N.Z.	1
Broad Red Clover	1
Chicory	6
Broad-leaved Plantain	3
Ribgrass	2
	24

Chicory and Plantain are two of the herbs which pigs will choose before all other ingredients of the ley. They are also probably the two most productive of the herbs included in these mixtures. This pig-grazing ley gives maximum yield of the leafy, high-protein, mineral-efficient herbs so important in the prevention of piglet anaemia and other deficiency diseases. Sows and litters grazing a mixture of this kind are unlikely to succumb to such troubles. Store pigs and dry sows can be maintained entirely on such a pasture through the summer months.

DREDGE-CORN AND SILAGE MIXTURES

Silage or Dredge-Corn Mixture
Double Purpose Mixture

For cutting green as silage or harvesting for grain and feeding-straw.

For High Protein Dredge Corn			*Lower Protein, but more certain on poorer land*	
lb. an acre			*lb. an acre*	
Oats	84		Oats	84
Beans	56		Wheat	28
Barley	28	or	Beans	14
Maple Peas	14		Barley	28
			Peas	14
	182			168

May be sown in autumn or spring so long as varieties of each ingredient are chosen specifically for the season of sowing.

SILAGE OR HAY MIXTURE
(for spring sowing)

	lb. an acre
Spring Oats	140
Maple Peas	28
	168

ARABLE SILAGE MIXTURE

The heaviest single-cut silage crop on all soils, which also leaves large quantities of nitrogen in the soil for subsequent crops.

	lb. an acre
Vetches or Tares	56
Oats	112
	168

SILAGE-GRAZING MIXTURE

An excellent two-year ley mixture, developed from a mixture I had originally from the pioneers of Elliot mixtures, Hunters of Chester. This mixture is very quick to establish, produces a great bulk of grazing or silage, and quickly recoversfrom grazing. It has a life of not more than two years of really effective production, though it can be left longer for grazing if necessary.

(Heavy Cut of Silage and two-year Grazing)

	lb. an acre
Westerwolth's Express Ryegrass	13
New Zealand H.1. Short-rotation Ryegrass	8
Certified Aberystwyth S.26 Cocksfoot (Hay- grazing strain)	6
Chicory (leafy)	3
S.100 White Clover	1
Broad Red Clover	1
	32

Sown at the end of August the above mixture will produce a heavy silage cut in May and be ready for grazing or a second cut in early July.

179

Winter Grazing Mixture

(to be sown in July)

An excellent insurance against shortage of conserved fodder.

	lb. an acre
Thousand-headed Kale	2
Hardy Green Turnips	2½
Italian Ryegrass	14
	18½

CHAPTER XVIII

Infertility in Cattle—A Warning

Is the Ley a Cause?

The modern ley has often been blamed for sterility, temporary infertility, and other breeding troubles in the herd; and there is no doubt that breeding failures are far more common on the farms of the foremost ley users. The man who boasts of his leys, their productivity and stock-carrying capacity, is often also the man who is having difficulty in getting his cows in calf. There is no doubt his leys *are* largely the cause of his troubles; but not because they are temporary pastures, as distinct from the old grazing pastures which did not seem to leave the cattle shy of breeding. No, it is the manner of managing the leys which causes the sterility; and, if persisted in, may well result in the extinction of the bovine race.

The main causes of the sterility which results from the temporary pasture are: (1) The lack of variety in the modern simple seeds' mixture; and especially the predominance of shallow-rooting ingredients, the roots of which draw their sustenance only from the seriously deficient top soil and supply none of the mineral-and trace-element needs of the breeding animal. (2) The inordinate use of soluble chemical fertilizers to stimulate 'early bite' and repeated forced growths of grazing or mowing grass; especially in conjunction with the electric fence and strip-grazing, which concentrates a large number of cattle on a small area of land, and limits the possibility of selective grazing whereby the cow could increase the variety of her diet.

Learned scientists have sought to isolate the factor in the ley which may be the cause of sterility; conferences have considered the problem. A variety of factors have come under suspicion including an excessive proportion of clover in the ley—especially S.100 White Clover—and ergot-infested ryegrass or cocksfoot. One veterinary surgeon even mooted the probability

181

that the excessive and frequent use of nitrogenous fertilizers is the most potent anti-fertility factor in the nutrition of the cow.

In my experience of visiting many farms in an effort to trace the cause of infertility in their cattle, there are but two factors associated with ley farming which are, either both together or each singly, potent causes of infertility: the fertilizer bag and the seeds mixture; cutting out the first and increasing the variety of the second has in every instance put an end to breeding troubles.

I end this book, therefore, with this warning to my fellow ley farmers. Whatever you accept or reject in this book, there is one practice you will continue only at the future peril of your herd. That is the feeding of breeding animals, whether they are dairy cows, beef cattle, sheep, pigs or poultry, on pastures which have been directly treated in the establishment, or top-dressed during growing, with chemical fertilizers of any description. By chemical fertilizer I mean the synthetic water-soluble fertilizers, manufactured or rendered soluble by the ingenuity of man; or the by-products of industry.

There is so much confusion about what is an artificial or chemical fertilizer or manure and what is an organic fertilizer or manure, that I venture to give my definitions; and, at the risk of disagreement among experts, organic and inorganic alike, I will divide all the commonly used fertilizers into the two categories: *organic,* which will include all those which for want of a better description are acceptable and beneficial to the soil and crop, and are used in the organic method; and *chemical* or *artificial,* which I consider unacceptable and in most cases harmful to soil, soil organisms, crops and the ultimate consumer. Some of the fertilizers in the organic section are actually inorganic rocks; but the term 'organic' does not refer only to the manures used, but to the methods employed in building and maintaining fertility, as distinct from the use of artificial stimulants which make no contribution to soil fertility—though it may be claimed by the chemist that they do feed the crop.

Without considering for this purpose whether the 'food' is good or bad, I do not dispute that the soluble chemical manure 'feeds' the crop. It is the very fact that it does stimulate the crop *directly* instead of sustaining the crop *through the organized biological processes of the soil* that excludes it from the *organic* method. The word 'organic' in this context describes the constructive application of natural biological processes to build and maintain fertility, using organic fertilizers, green manures and natural inorganic rock (pulverized for convenience). The 'chemical' method, on the other hand, includes all synthetic soluble soil and crop-stimulants prepared by chemical treatment; and the waste by-products of industry disorganized or removed from natural context by processing other than simple grinding.

An example of a product accepted by some so-called 'organic' farmers, but which I believe is not organic according to the foregoing definition, is Basic Slag. To quote Fisons' *Fertilizer Book,* basic slag is produced 'in the conversion of pig-iron into steel'. Slag is produced in the furnaces from the phosphorus present asan impurity in the pig-iron. 'The phosphate in slag is present in complex chemical form which is insoluble in water, but partly soluble in a 2 percent solution of citric acid.' But as it is insoluble in water and therefore released slowly by the soil acids, basic slag may be regarded as a borderline fertilizer. The evidence against it is certainly less than against any other artificial fertilizer in my own assessment; and my judgment against using it (quite apart from the wastefulness of *buying* phosphates at all when they can be got for nothing by the organic method described in this book) is based only on the fact that it was almost the only fertilizer in use on my farm in the early days of disease in stock and crops described in my earlier books.

In listing materials used for manurial purposes I prefer in my own mind to call those natural manures and ground rocks which genuinely add fertility to the soil, their rightful name of 'fertilizer' (contributors of fertility); and the synthetic soil stimulants (which *reduce* the inherent fertility of the soil by depressing biological processes) '*de*fertilizers' or simply 'soil stimulants.'

ORGANIC METHOD

Genuine Fertilizers

Farmyard manure or organic compost

Green crop manures

Raw Sewage Sludge and *Sewage Powder*

Seaweed and *Seaweed Fertilizer Pure Fish Manure*
  (Sometimes adulterated with Sulphate of Ammonia, so ask about this before ordering.)

CHEMICAL METHOD

Defertilizers or Soil Stimulants

Sulphate of Ammonia

There are two sources of supply, viz. from gas-works and coke-oven plants, and from synthetic ammonia factories. In the first case the ammonia driven off from the coal is neutralized with sulphuric acid, and in the second case nitrogen from the air is made to combine with hydrogen to form ammonia which is then reacted with anhydrite (calcium sulphate) or with sulphuric acid to give the final product.

183

ORGANIC METHOD
—CONTINUED

Hoof and Horn Meal

Meat, blood and bone manures

Shoddy—wool wastes

Ground Rock Phosphate, or *Mineral Rock Phosphate*

Rock phosphates are found as soft rock formations in several parts of the world; but those in Morocco, Tunisia, and Algeria provide practically all the raw phosphate used in Western Europe. The rock deposits are, with one or two exceptions, of marine origin, and consist of calcium phosphate (fluorapatite) and calcium carbonate.

Granite dust and other pulverized rocks

CHEMICAL METHOD
—CONTINUED

Nitrate of Soda

Most of the Nitrate of Soda today is manufactured synthetically by oxidizing ammonia to nitric acid, which is then neutralized with soda.

Nitro-Chalk

Manufactured by mixing ammonium nitrate with precipitated chalk.

Superphosphate

This fertilizer was the first 'manufactured' or 'chemical' fertilizer, and is produced by treating ground rock phosphate with sulphuric acid.

Triple Superphosphate

Manufactured by treating rock phosphate with a solution of phosphoric acid instead of sulphuric acid. The phosphoric acid is first prepared by treating rock phosphate with a slight excess of sulphuric acid and then separating the gypsum (calcium sulphate).

CHEMICAL METHOD
—CONTINUED

Sulphate of Potash

    Produced by treating
Muriate of Potash with
sulphuric acid.

Muriate of Potash

    Produced from the natural
potash salt deposits found
in Germany, Alsace,
Spain and Palestine, by a
crystallization process.

Basic Slag

    A by-product of the steel
furnaces.

Source or method of
manufacture in each case
is quoted from Fisons'
Fertilizer Book.

Resources

Below are updated contact points mentioned by N. Turner that are still in existence today. The avid student will no doubt turn up additional sources.

The Soil Association, South Plaza, Marlborough Street, Bristol BS1 3NX, United Kingdom, phone 0117-314-5000, website *www.soilassociation.org.*

Cotswold Seed Ltd. [Herbal Ley Seed Distributor], Cotswold Business Village, Moreton-in-Marsh, Gloucestershire GL56 0JQ, United Kingdom, website *www.cotswoldseeds.co.uk/herballeys.htm.*

ANIMAL HEALTH ASSOCIATIONS

United States Animal Health Association, P.O. Box 8805, St Joseph, Missouri 64508, phone 816-671-1144, website *www.usaha.org.*

Institute for Animal Health, Compton Laboratory, Compton, Newbury, Berks RG20 7NN, United Kingdom, website *www.iah.bbsrc.ac.uk.*

New Zealand Association for Animal Health and Crop Protection, P.O. Box 5069, Wellington, New Zealand, website *www1.agcarm.co.nz.*

Animal Health Alliance Ltd., Level 2, AMP Building, 1 Hobart Place, Canberra, ACT 2601, Australia, website *www.animalhealthalliance.org.au.*

DEXTER CATTLE SOCIETIES

American Dexter Cattle Association, 4150 Merino Avenue, Watertown, Minnesota 55388, phone 952-215-2206, website *www.dextercattle.org.*

The Dexter Cattle Society, 1st Floor, RASE Offices, Stoneleigh Park, Warks CV8 2LZ, United Kingdom, phone 0247-669-2300, website *www.dextercattle.co.uk.*

Dexter Cattle Society New Zealand, 92A Takanini-Clevedon Road, Ardmore, RD 2, Papakura, Aukland, New Zealand, website *www.dexter-cattle.co.nz.*

Dexters—Beefy Little Milkers, ABRI—University of New England, Armidale, NSW 2351, Australia, website *dexter.une.edu.au.*

Index

INDEX

INDEX

Also by Newman Turner

Fertility Farming
by Newman Turner

 *Fertility Farming* explores an approach to farming that makes minimal use of plowing, eschews chemical fertilizers and pesticides, and emphasizes soil fertility via crop rotation, composting, cover cropping and manure application.

Turner holds that the foundation of the effectiveness of nature's husbandry is a fertile soil — and the measure of a fertile soil is its content of organic matter, ultimately, its *humus.* Upon a basis of humus, nature builds a complete structure of healthy life — without need for disease control of any kind. In fact, disease treatment is unnecessary in nature, as disease is the outcome of the unbalancing or perversion of the natural order — and serves as a warning that something is wrong. The avoidance of disease is therefore the simple practice of natural law. Much more than theory, this book was written to serve as a practical guide for farmers. Turner's advice for building a productive, profitable organic farming system rings as true today as it did sixty years ago when it was written. *Softcover, 272 pages. ISBN 978-1-601730-09-1*

Herdsmanship
by Newman Turner

 In this book, Turner explains that livestock illness is a result of bad farming practices and that real livestock health begins with true natural farming disciplines such as composting, biodiverse pastures with deep-rooted forages and herbs, and sub-soiling, as well as the avoidance of supposed panaceas that ignore or marginalize these fundamentals such as vaccines, pesticides, antibiotics and artificial fertilizers. He teaches that the cornerstones of profitability are rooted in herd health, which in turn is rooted in: soil fertility and animal nutrition, cattle breeding for better feed efficiency, and cattle breeding for longevity. Longevity, he holds, is the most critical factor for success in livestock breeding and production. *Softcover, 272 pages. ISBN 978-1-601730-10-7*

Cure Your Own Cattle
by Newman Turner

 In this booklet, Newman Turner sought to "bring within the reach of the farmer a solution to his disease problems in a way in which drug and chemical treatments have never before achieved." He relied on his lifetime of observing animals and herbs in their natural environment to guide him in his experiments. The end result is his proclamation that freedom from animal diseases may be attained by the proper utilization of nature's provisions. While the subject of natural veterinary care has grown and matured, Turner's clear and simple systems and advice remind farmers of the true fundamentals that consistently work. *Softcover, 96 pages. ISBN 978-1-601730-08-4*

Also from Acres U.S.A.

Eco-Farm: An Acres U.S.A. Primer
by Charles Walters

In this book, eco-agriculture is explained — from the tiniest molecular building blocks to managing the soil — in terminology that not only makes the subject easy to learn, but vibrantly alive. Sections on NP&K, cation exchange capacity, composting, Brix, soil life, and more! *Eco-Farm* truly delivers a complete education in soils, crops, and weed and insect control. This should be the first book read by everyone beginning in eco-agriculture . . . and the most shop-worn book on the shelf of the most experienced.
Softcover, 476 pages. ISBN 978-0-911311-74-7

Weeds: Control Without Poisons
by Charles Walters

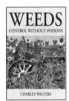

For a thorough understanding of the conditions that produce certain weeds, you simply can't find a better source than this one — certainly not one as entertaining, as full of anecdotes and homespun common sense. It contains a lifetime of collected wisdom that teaches us how to understand and thereby control the growth of countless weed species, as well as why there is an absolute necessity for a more holistic, eco-centered perspective in agriculture today. Contains specifics on a hundred weeds, why they grow, what soil conditions spur them on or stop them, what they say about your soil, and how to control them without the obscene presence of poisons, all cross-referenced by scientific and various common names, and a new pictorial glossary. *Softcover, 352 pages. ISBN 978-0-911311-58-7*

The Biological Farmer
A Complete Guide to the Sustainable & Profitable Biological System of Farming
by Gary F. Zimmer

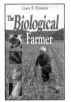

Biological farmers work with nature, feeding soil life, balancing soil minerals, and tilling soils with a purpose. The methods they apply involve a unique system of beliefs, observations and guidelines that result in increased production and profit. This practical how-to guide elucidates their methods and will help you make farming fun and profitable. *The Biological Farmer* is the farming consultant's bible. It schools the interested grower in methods of maintaining a balanced, healthy soil that promises greater productivity at lower costs, and it covers some of the pitfalls of conventional farming practices. Zimmer knows how to make responsible farming work. His extensive knowledge of biological farming and consulting experience come through in this complete, practical guide to making farming fun and profitable. *Softcover, 352 pages. ISBN 978-0-911311-62-4*

To order call 1-800-355-5313 or order online at www.acresusa.com